STEPPY

THE KID IN THE 10 SHIRT

Steppy UK Ltd 2018

First published in paperback in Great Britain by
Steppy UK Ltd. 3 Knighton Hayes Hall, 6C
Ratcliffe Road, Leicester. LE2 3TB

This publication 2019

Copyright © 2018
Steppy UK Ltd
Mike and Susanna Steptoe
Cover Design © Kay Quilter

ISBN 978-1-5272-3559-5

To history - when dreams became reality in
the shadow of Table Mountain

Contents

1.

Debut – Old Trafford

With their final away game at Chelsea on Sunday, this would have to be United's night of glory in front of a capacity crowd of 76,000 at Old Trafford, and a huge worldwide TV audience. United needed only three points to take the title and continue their reign as champions. They were looking for their twelfth consecutive home win.

It was the last Monday night football match of the Premier League season. Southford City were fighting for survival in their first year in the top tier of the football league. With two games to go for both competing clubs, Southford needed three points to be sure of Premier League football next season. Both teams had everything to play for…

At the morning pre-match press conference, the United Manager seemed very confident, as he had a full squad to select from. Their recent form had been excellent, with six wins out of six games going into this match. His counterpart at Southford was nowhere near as upbeat, as they had been plagued by injuries in recent weeks and had lost their last two games. Nevertheless, they had a very strong football philosophy and were not prepared to change it.

Rumour was rife in the packed pressroom that Southford might debut a young fifteen-year-old local boy, making him the youngest ever player to play in the Premier League. Roald Katza, the Manager of Southford, refused to confirm or deny the rumour. There was a real buzz of anticipation in the room.

"Wait and see tonight!" Katza answered, as he brought the interview to a close.

The player that they were talking about was Danny Cook - Deco to his friends. He mysteriously appeared (almost out of nowhere) when he played in the Under-15 Milk Cup Tournament in Northern Ireland the previous summer. It was the first time Southford had entered a competition that included the two Manchester clubs, as well as Ajax of Amsterdam, Anderlecht, Bayern Munich, and Sporting Lisbon. These were clubs with elite Category 1 academies – giants in youth development. Deco had been the standout player of the tournament, attracting attention from all the scouts. His parents had been inundated with enquiries from most of the top European Clubs yet had chosen for him to stay with Southford.

Although Deco had only just arrived on the football scene, his exploits in the Milk Cup had already earned him three caps for the England Schoolboys Under-15 team. One of the games against Sweden was played in front of 34,000 spectators at Wembley a few weeks ago. The game was televised on satellite TV, and everyone was raving about this Deco who played the 10-position, just behind the top striker. He was exceptional and was voted Man of the Match after scoring a hat-trick.

There was a real buzz in the Old Trafford stadium as it began to fill. Southford had sold their full allocation of tickets, with many of their fans thinking that they may never get the opportunity to see their team play at Old Trafford again. With a quarter of an hour to go before kick-off, Deco's Mum, Dad, younger brother and his two best friends took their seats near the Directors' Box. The teams had already been announced half an hour earlier, and Deco would be starting in his familiar 10-position. The press photographers were surrounding them – click, click, clicking away, as his family sat down to soak up the atmosphere.

"Just how good *is* your son, Mr Cook?" one photographer asked Deco's dad. But as the question was being asked, the press photographers were quickly ushered away by the stewards.

The Cook family arrived at the stadium early so that they wouldn't need to queue. They sat together in the main stand, each with a match programme gripped nervously in hand. Deco's best friends, Gheorghe Mutu and his twin sister Nadia, sat in the two seats immediately in front of them. Both of the twins were good footballers and had also represented England at Under-15 level. Nadia was a revelation when she played for the schoolgirls, and Gheorghe made a good impression when he made his debut off the bench in the game against Sweden. The twins and Deco had been best friends since the age of eight.

"Just how good is he?" Sarah whispered to Joe. "This is my precious, little boy playing against some of the best players in the world... Grown men! Superstars! Everything seems a bit surreal."

"He's good ... very good, and despite his age and size he can look after himself. Don't worry, my love," Joe smiled, squeezing her hand to reassure her.

"Don't worry, Doc! He's too smart to get caught by anyone," chirped Nadia, who had razor-sharp hearing, as she turned around and warmly reassured Sarah further. Sarah smiled and put her hand on Nadia's shoulder.

By now the stadium was full, and the atmosphere was electric as the United faithful celebrated in anticipation of being crowned Champions that very night. The ground erupted as the two teams came out of the tunnel. The Cook party stood in an effort to see Deco as he filed out, last but one, for the Southford team. Sarah thought how small he looked compared to the height of the United giants, who were all over 185 cm – 'six-footers', as they were known.

They lined up on the halfway line with the press photographers seemingly focused on the young Deco, who looked nervous as their cameras clicked repeatedly. He looked around at the vast stands and the capacity crowd, briefly thinking back in time to playing on his 'football pitch-lawn' and dreaming about victory against United. He was brought back to reality as the United team strode by and shook hands. One or two big-named players encouraged him by wishing him good luck.

"Bonne chance!" the smiling French midfielder nodded at Deco. He was a giant of a man at 1.91m, and ruffled Deco's hair as they shook hands.

Both teams ran off to continue their warm-up. The Southford team received an enthusiastic reception from their travelling fans as they warmed up in front of them. Deco's nerves were beginning to settle now, and he couldn't wait to get the game underway.

United won the toss and elected to attack the Stretford end, so the teams changed ends. Southford were attacking the goal to the left of their fans. Deco received the ball straight from kick-off and calmly played a diagonal ball across to his right-side midfield teammate. Southford lined up with a traditional four-four-two, though Deco was more forward at the top of the diamond position to provide a link between the two attackers and the midfielders, and to give support to his striker as a number 10.

Southford went immediately on the attack, and the midfielders raced to support the two strikers.

With almost everyone committed forward in the typically uncompromising Southford style, United took possession through their physical French midfielder, who played a great ball through to their speedy striker, who in turn took it in his stride and hit an unstoppable shot past the despairing dive of the Southford keeper. It was 1–0 United after one minute!

United pressurised the Southford defence relentlessly until the fortieth minute. Wave after wave of attacks forced Deco into a more defensive role than everyone expected. The competition was now intense. Joe was pleased with the way his son was applying himself in getting back behind the ball.

"He's having to play your game, Mutu!" he joked with Gheorghe.

Deco stole the ball again and quickly moved it forward to his striker. He controlled the ball with one touch, as Deco moved expertly to receive the return. Out of the corner of his eye, he saw the Frenchman coming and skipped over his lunging right leg like a ballet dancer. In one movement, he checked and played the ball just over the top of the United defence. The Southford striker ran onto it and found himself one-on-one with the United keeper. He dispatched the ball into the far corner of the net, giving the keeper no chance. United had enjoyed sixty per cent possession in the first half and this was the only attempt on goal for Southford. 1–1 as the half-time whistle blew.

Deco had done okay. Actually, better than okay. He was the outstanding player for Southford in the first half, and he achieved his first ever assist in the Premier League!

The second half started at a frantic pace. United were totally committed to winning this game and maintained their domination through possession. Southford defended resolutely but found it difficult in the transition from defence to attack. Deco was the exception as he always posed a threat on the break, so much so that the Frenchman had clearly been designated to keep an eye on him.

After seventy minutes, with the score still one-all, United hit the bar with a header from the Frenchman. The ball was headed with brute force; it ricocheted back outside of the penalty area to where Deco was prowling unmarked. Although well into his own half, he only had three players between him and the United keeper. He reacted instinctively, collected the ball, and with one touch, went past the first defender. The other two were now backing off as he moved forward at lightning pace. The defenders closed together, and the left full-back was the first to pressure Deco, trying to close him down and push him to his left touchline. Deco, determined to leave him for dead, changed feet and cut inside. The centre-back panicked and committed himself far too early, missing his tackle and leaving Deco one-on-one with the keeper. Deco nonchalantly placed the ball in the far corner of the net. There was a deathly hush...

The kid had ruined the party! 1–2 Southford.

Deco's family and the Mutu twins were on their feet cheering. The crowds around were silent, although a few of them clapped to show their appreciation for Deco's skill. His teammates mobbed him and then quickly returned to their positions for the restart.

As the game recommenced, Roald Katza made a substitution, bringing on a defender for the top-striker. Southford were forced to defend deep and were under constant pressure from the United front line. They missed two golden opportunities; the keeper made one fantastic save and they hit the upright with a gaping goal.

As the game reached the ninetieth minute, the fourth official indicated a minimum of four minutes to be added on. The Frenchman, spurred to action by the time ticking away, picked up the ball on the edge of the area, beat one man and hit a right-footer beneath the diving goalkeeper. The whole ground erupted. United were famed for late goals and here it was! 2–2.

Southford lost the ball from the restart and came under pressure again. They had one minute left to survive for the draw. However, Deco had a different agenda as he received the ball out on the left, with at least four defenders between him and goal. He had no support, so just turned and jinked past the first defender and took the next one out with a feint and change of feet in the other direction. He was twenty-five yards out when the Frenchman aggressively scythed him down from behind. It came as a shock as Deco hadn't seen him coming. It earned a booking for the tackle and left Southford with a direct free kick just outside the penalty box.

There was no question who was going to take the free kick – the rest of the team had seen Deco's free kicks in practice. This would probably be the last action of the game. The opposing wall lined up while Deco placed the ball, opting to take the kick with his right foot. There was a spooky silence as he started his short, straight run up. He hit the ball up and over the wall, and into the keeper's top left corner.

"GOOOAAAAAAAAAAAL!" the Monday night football TV commentator screamed, as Deco blasted the ball into the roof of the net.

"Deco Cook scores the winner for Southford with the final kick of the game!"

2.

The Transfer

Seven years earlier...

It was late in the morning when the car finally pulled away from outside the house in Southford. The removal van had already left an hour earlier, crammed to the roof with all of the Cook family's furniture and belongings.

It had taken over half an hour to squeeze the L-shaped sofa in, and Mrs Cook had been visibly distressed at the prospect of having to leave it behind. Danny had stood watching as her face twisted into several funny expressions. It reminded him of the time when he had walked into the living room and seen her standing in front of the mirror, repeatedly sucking in her cheeks before letting out slow breaths. Dad had told him she was trying to work on her cheekbones. Danny hadn't really understood what his dad meant but could tell Dad thought it was a silly thing for his mum to be doing.

Danny, who had spent the morning watching his mum and dad run around like headless chickens, was now sitting miserably in the back of the car next to Baby Ben, his nine-month-old brother, who was safely strapped into his car seat. Baby Ben was asleep again. Danny couldn't understand how Baby Ben could sleep through such chaos, especially on an occasion as important as their BIG MOVE.

Danny looked back down the street towards his old house that was now starting to look like a small dot on the horizon, and tears rolled quietly down his cheeks. He really, really, *really* didn't want to leave. In fact, he had begged his parents to change their minds. He had sincerely promised to unload the dishwasher *every* day until his eighteenth birthday if he could persuade them to stay in Southford. Their continual response was to pat him on the head, as if he were a dog, and reassure him that everything would be all right.

His mum even said he was her 'little soldier'. Danny found this quite annoying, as he certainly didn't feel like everything would be all right, and he most certainly didn't feel like a soldier!

His mum, Sarah, was a doctor, and since finishing her maternity leave, had been working part-time at Southford General Hospital. Actually, she was the reason they were moving away from Southford, a big, bustling city, to a new address in Glenrise, a boring, sleepy village an hour away. Sarah was going to work full-time as a doctor at Glenrise Medical Centre, and the Cooks were going to move to their new house which was next door, sandwiched between the Medical Centre and Glenrise Primary School. Danny thought it sounded *awful*, and certainly didn't want to be stuck somewhere close to where ill people would be turning up at all times of the day, puking and sniffling and needing medicine. He also didn't want to be reminded of school every time he set foot outside his front door.

Danny's dad, Joe Cook, was also going to start a new job. In fact, two new jobs! He was going to become house dad for Danny and Baby Ben and was also going to be starting his own business as a part-time football coach, based at the nearby school.

Joe had been a brilliant footballer up until a few years ago when, at the age of twenty-three, he had injured his knee and was forced to stop playing. Joe frequently told Danny the story of the nasty sliding tackle that had finished his career, but Sarah had recently banned him from telling it at the dinner table, as she said it made her feel nauseous. Danny didn't know what that meant but didn't think it was a positive word, as Sarah wrinkled her nose every time she said it.

Since his injury, Joe had worked in an office and hated every minute of it. When he finished work each day, he would practically rip off his suit as soon as he walked through the front door. He once told Danny that his tie was like a rope around his neck. Joe spent all of his spare time studying to achieve his football coaching badges and had finally qualified as a Level 3 UEFA B Licence coach last month.

Danny wasn't sure what all those letters meant, but knew it was something really impressive as his mum and dad had celebrated at a local restaurant, and even had champagne! Much to Joe's delight, this achievement meant that his stuffy suits had now been donated to the charity shop, and he now had a new daily uniform – a tracksuit, which he seemed to love so much that he never took it off. Joe was really looking forward to his new life in Glenrise, and Danny had noticed that he had developed a slight spring in his step.

To be fair, Danny could understand the opportunities for both his mum and dad in Glenrise. Nevertheless, he didn't want to sacrifice his friendships or his football club, and thought it was a bit scary to be going to a different, foreign-seeming place.

It was only yesterday that he had been playing in the school playground on his last day of Year 3.

All his friends were extremely excited because they could trial for the school football team once they were in Year 4. Danny was no different – he had been looking forward to that day virtually since he could first kick a ball, and had spent every break time and lunchtime practising, even when it had poured with rain. He had even flagged it up on the kitchen calendar. Now it would never happen.

He had been transferred against his will.

Danny was small, wiry and exceptionally fast, and, although he was now eight years old, he had never played in an organised football team before. His dad enrolled him at an after-school club at the age of five, where they practised with a small ball and were taught special skills. When he had asked to join a proper team, his dad had told him that he mustn't try to run before he could walk. Danny thought this was a bit of an odd thing to say, as he had been both walking and running for years, but when Danny mentioned this fact to Joe, he merely chuckled and ruffled Danny's hair.

"You'll appreciate what it means one day, son," Joe answered.

Danny had exercised and trained for six hours a week at the after-school club, and 9am to 1pm on most weekdays of the school holidays at the holiday club. He loved every minute of it. He dreamed of becoming the next Ronaldo or Messi, and his room in Southford had been covered in pictures of his favourite football idols. His grandad had even brought a scarf back from Barcelona for him, and Danny had hung it proudly above his bed, hoping that one day he would not only wear the scarf, but the full kit too, running out to screaming fans at the Nou Camp.

Everywhere Danny went he took a small tennis ball with him and would kick it around pretending to be one of his heroes. Sarah blamed him for ruining all the plants in their back garden and had given up on buying more as she knew Danny was never going to stop kicking his football around, no matter how many times she banished him to the Naughty Step.

When Danny was born, his dad had wanted to name him after *his* all-time hero who had played for Porto, Barcelona and Chelsea – a Brazilian-born, Portuguese player called Deco. Sarah would have none of it, insisting that he be named after her own dad who was called Daniel. She did let Joe choose a middle name, as long as it wasn't after a footballer. She was to regret that very soon afterwards when it was decided that Danny's middle name would be Edward. Daniel Edward Cook – DECo.

Joe was very pleased with himself. He had managed to outwit Sarah and get his own way. That didn't occur too often in the Cook household! Danny had been called by his nickname, Deco, ever since. Well, by everyone except Mum, of course, who still insisted on calling him Daniel. Or, when she was in a bad mood like this morning, Daniel Edward Cook…

3.

The Arrival

As far as Deco was concerned, the journey to Glenrise had lasted for hours. He was even starting to feel a little car sick, and it didn't help that Baby Ben had woken up and was eating stinky cheddar biscuits. The smell was too much for Deco, who was cramped up next to Baby Ben's car seat alongside a pile of cushions that hadn't fitted into the removal van. The cushion material was irritating Deco as it kept brushing against his arm. He rolled down his window and tried to breathe in gulps of fresh air, feeling more miserable than ever.

He had visited Glenrise once before with Mum, Dad and Baby Ben, but the journey seemed a zillion times longer now, and even back then it had been a complete *nightmare*. He remembered being dragged there one day back in February after school. The light was fading, and it was raining heavily. "Aren't we there yet?" he grumbled constantly.

"We will be in five minutes, son," Dad would say each time he asked the question.

Deco lost track of the number of times he had counted five lots of sixty seconds, so had slumped back in the seat and stared out of the car glumly. When they had eventually arrived in Glenrise, the village looked dark and dreary, and there was no one to be seen apart from two old grannies at the bus stop with their shopping trollies and umbrellas.

Weirdly, as the Cook car navigated its way into the village today, Deco didn't recognise it – the sun had popped out from behind the clouds and, much to Deco's surprise, everywhere was bright with the greenery of the trees and beautifully coloured flowers. There were no grannies at the bus stop either, though there were several children on scooters (racing ahead of their nattering mums), down a gentle, winding hill.

There was even an ice cream van up ahead and, although he wouldn't admit it to his parents, the thought of an ice cream van regularly stopping so close to their new home was a tiny bit exciting, especially if, when Mum was at work, Dad would let him have a 99 with a flake and *raspberry sauce*.

As their car entered the main hub of the village and approached a traffic island, Deco saw the new housing estate on his right. It seemed to stretch back as far as the eye could see. The builders were still building the new properties but weren't working as it was a Saturday.

Saturday…

This was when Deco usually played football in the garden at their old house in Southford, before watching the teatime match on Sky, followed by *The X Factor*. (He didn't think *The X Factor* was very interesting really, but it was an excuse to stay up later than usual, and he enjoyed feeling cosy, cocooned between Mum and Dad on the L-shaped sofa).

There was another smaller, older estate of houses on the left, followed by a really pretty village green, with a variety of small shops of various kinds. Next, there was an enormous, ancient-looking, centuries-old church with a spire and a clock. Attached to the church was a small cemetery. As they went past, the clock made Deco and Baby Ben jump as the chimes struck loudly. Baby Ben giggled, but Deco was still trying to show his parents how unhappy he was, so pretended to be disinterested. He scowled at his younger brother for not doing the same.

There was a supermarket, a butcher and a post office all facing onto the green, and a large single-storey wooden building, with a sloping roof, which was next door to the church. Outside there was a big, black noticeboard with the words 'Parish Hall' written across the top. Sarah turned to Deco and pointed at the hall, telling him that she had heard it was where a lot of the local children held their birthday parties. This made Deco a little curious as Dad had suggested that he could have a football party for his ninth birthday. He looked back over his shoulder at it, and started sizing up the hall, wondering if it would be big enough. He hoped desperately that it would at least have room for a boisterous game of five-a-side.

As they drove on, Deco noticed that everyone seemed to know each other. People were smiling and chatting and looked very at ease in their summer clothes. It reminded Deco of the time his parents held a barbecue back in Southford. It had been a really sunny day, with everyone laughing and joking, and Mum had been in such a good mood she had let him have his own can of Pepsi. He'd felt really grown-up and had told all his friends at school about it. He'd loved that day.

Deco briefly stopped reminiscing about the good old days in Southford. He had spotted some Glenrise boys wearing football shirts. He saw the black and white stripes of Newcastle United, the red of Liverpool, at least two Barcelona shirts, and the inevitable, unmistakable red of Man United. It didn't matter where he went, there would always be a Man United fan, even though Manchester was more than 100 miles away from Glenrise. 'Glory seekers' Dad always called them, reckoning that the people who actually had tickets to watch Man United were more interested in the half-time prawns than the football, and that real Man United fans could only dream of visiting Old Trafford on a match day. That struck Deco as quite odd, especially that people ate prawns at a football game. When *he* went to football matches with his dad, *he* always had a burger...

Deco was still in a strop, especially when he realised the football shirts were the only symbol of normality he had seen all morning.

They drove slowly past the shops and through rows of streets on both sides of the road. These were very different properties to the ones he had seen on the way into the village. They reminded him of some of the streets in Southford near to the Southford City football ground – terraced houses with front doors facing straight onto the pavement, houses on top of houses, or so it seemed. It brought back memories of match days when he and Dad would walk down the streets leading to the ground.

He suddenly realised that this was *another* part of life in Southford he'd miss. His mental list, that he had called 'The best things about Southford', was getting so long that he was starting to forget the first few points on it. He knew he would miss Southford City maybe even more than his old house, even more than his old school and *even more* than his old friends. Although Southford didn't play in the Premier League, they were *his* team, and the *only* team he ever wanted to play for in England. He felt the tears coming back, but decided he needed to fight them off.

It had been a strange journey. Mum and Dad hadn't been very talkative, and Baby Ben had slept nearly the whole way. The houses on both sides of the road changed again. They appeared to be bigger and more spaced out with separate entrances, yet still old. There was a petrol station with a convenience store on the left, and a Costa

Coffee shop opposite. He looked at Mum to see if she was smiling – even back in Southford she used to say Costa was her 'little treat'.

Further along, on the right, he could see a large new building with a sign clearly visible – 'Glenrise Medical Centre'. He realised that when Mum was at work, she would be able to leave all the ill people for a few minutes and nip across the road to Costa for a much-needed break. Even though he was still cross, Deco was also a little bit pleased for her, as he knew his mum worked very hard to make people better, which sometimes made her extremely tired and ratty. Dad often joked that she only became human after her caffeine fix.

Just past the Medical Centre, he saw the big, black removal van that was loaded with their furniture earlier that morning. The ramp on the back had been lowered, and the van was already half unloaded. It was parked outside a big house that he had once overheard his mum describe to his aunt as a Victorian detached. He hadn't a clue what that meant but remembered learning something about the Victorians in a history topic at school. His teacher had said something about rich Victorian families having male and female servants.

As far as he knew, the Cook family probably weren't going to have any servants, so he was still baffled as to what a Victorian detached could possibly be. He could see their new house was just like the other houses on the street, and presumed he would eventually find out the meaning of his mum's strange description...

"Well, this is it then!" Dad announced. "What do you think of your new home?"

Deco had only seen photos of the house on the Internet, as he hadn't gone with his parents when they viewed the house before, and so he wasn't quite sure what to say in response. His parents were clearly excited as the car pulled into the short driveway to the house, but Deco's stomach was lurching, his heart was beating way too quickly, and he felt a bit awkward and out of sorts as everything was so unfamiliar.

As he stepped out of the car, Deco forced himself to be brave and look up at their new house. He was worried that he would forget the old one if he looked at the new one for too long. It was bigger than it seemed on the photos, and actually far grander. Dad had described it as a real bargain compared to what it would have cost in Southford.

For the second time that day, Deco was quietly impressed. There were two huge bay windows, one either side of the covered porch to the doorway. The porch had a sloping roof with two brick pillars supporting it. He could see two more big windows above the bay windows. He wondered if one might be his bedroom, and the lurching in his stomach began to give way to butterflies of nervous excitement.

To the left of the house there was a single garage set back along a gravel driveway, with a side entrance into the kitchen. It was through this doorway that they entered the house. Deco was instantly amazed at the size of the kitchen. It was probably twice as big as their old one, with fitted wooden worktops all around an enormous fridge that was the size of a front door. There was even a dining table with six chairs. He was very relieved to see that his new house could accommodate lots of people, especially Grandad and Grandma when they came to visit. At the old house, Dad would have to fetch two extra chairs out of the garage on Christmas Day so that Grandad and Grandma could enjoy their turkey, but now he wouldn't need to do that any more. It was dawning on him that there *might* be some good things about Glenrise after all.

He also noticed there were full-length double glass doors that opened onto the garden. The room was so bright! Deco could see out into the garden now and was gobsmacked by the size of it. If the Parish Hall wasn't available, or big enough for a football party, his new back garden certainly was! It faced the sun, and the length of the back lawn … it seemed to just go on forever and ever. Part of the lawn ran up to the side of the garage, and there was an old wooden shed behind it. Deco immediately thought of the dens he could make in the shed.

His mind instantly wandered back to football.

"That wall could be my goal," he thought. "If I have no friends to play with, at least I will have the wall to practise against." Suddenly, for the first time that day, a smile started to appear on his face as he contemplated the prospect of endless hours of pleasure playing football against the wall.

He concluded that Glenrise wasn't *so* bad, after all.

Mum led the way through from the kitchen into a large hallway with an open door opposite. The removal men were just coming in with Dad's massive flat screen TV. It was quite a weight. The TV was Dad's pride and joy, mainly because it enabled him and all the family to watch the football every Saturday and Sunday afternoon. He loved to watch famous players competing in the Premier League, and sometimes his beloved Southford City in the Championship. The TV was being manoeuvered into place, and he could picture sitting with Dad on the sofa, watching the start of the *new* season, in the *new* lounge, of their *new* house. Again, the room was very bright and airy, with a large, double patio door looking out onto (what Deco had already decided was) his 'football pitch of a lawn'.

Mum and Dad were now almost childlike and giddy as they showed the two boys around the rest of the house. Dad carried Baby Ben while Deco followed Mum from room to room, trying to take it all in. The dining room first, behind the kitchen, with the big bay window onto the front, and then a quick stop at the loo, through its doorway under the stairs, then up to the three bedrooms and the bathroom on the first floor. Baby Ben was to have the smaller room at the front, next to Mum and Dad's large bedroom that even had an en-suite shower and loo. Deco was to have the privilege of a bedroom that overlooked his football pitch-lawn, and already had his bed and cupboards positioned. It actually felt a little bit more like home.

Deco stood on his tiptoes and looked out beyond the lawn. He could see sports fields and a smart, new-looking building in the distance.

"What's that?" he asked.

"That's your school, and the village sports fields are next to it," Dad replied. Deco couldn't hide his excitement.

"And what's that?" he asked, pointing to what looked like a tennis court with a high fence and floodlights. Dad couldn't hide his excitement either.

"That's an all-weather AstroTurf surface where my new coaching business will be based."

"Wow!" Deco responded, now completely in awe of his new environment and all its wonderful surprises.

That night, once the removal men had left, Deco sat down at the new, enormous dining table and ate takeaway Hawaiian pizza with Mum and Dad. Mum was in such a good mood that she didn't even tell him off when he scraped his pineapple back into the box and just ate the ham.

Baby Ben had already had his bath and final feed of the day, so was snuggly wrapped up in his cot.

The disappointment and unhappiness of earlier had made Deco tired, so he was ready for bed soon after he had polished off his sixth slice of pizza. He was completely exhausted as he climbed the stairs and went to his new room, but also pleasantly relieved that the grey cloud, which had been hanging above his head when he'd said goodbye to Southford, was disappearing. He was beginning to think that maybe he could learn to like it here after all.

It didn't take him long to fall into a deep, satisfying sleep, where he dreamed of sailing across turquoise seas in a beautiful, big yacht near to the coast of Barcelona...

The transfer and arrival hadn't gone so badly after all.

4.

Football Pitch-Lawn

The next morning, Deco was rudely awakened by the loud but frustratingly familiar sound of Dad's petrol-driven lawn mower.

"What is it about adults and their boring routines?" he thought, groaning and trying to block out the continuous hum by shoving his pillow tightly over his head. Here they were, miles away from their old home in Southford, and yet Dad was *still* doing what he *always* did first thing on a Sunday morning – mowing the lawn in the hope that one day it would look like Wembley. It had a long way to go. Deco sighed deeply, realising the pillow wasn't blocking out any noise at all. In fact, it was just making it harder for him to breathe.

He suddenly perked up though, remembering that there was another part to his dad's routine on a Sunday, a part he quite enjoyed – the Full English.

He had no idea why it was called that, but he knew that if Dad was slogging himself silly mowing the lawn, he would be working up the appetite of a giant. It was certainly looking good for bacon, egg, bangers and beans ... and maybe even some hash browns or fried potatoes!

After a few minutes, the mower stopped and there was a long silence. Deco started to worry that maybe they wouldn't get a Full English in the new house after all, but his fears were unnecessary.

"Daniel, breakfast is ready!" Mum almost sang the delicious sentence just a couple of minutes later.

Whenever Deco heard the word 'breakfast' on a Sunday, he was no longer Messi, but rather, Usain Bolt. He did everything at lightning speed – he didn't want to risk Dad eating all the hash browns or fried potatoes before he managed his own pick of the spread.

Every Sunday he prided himself on setting a new personal best, especially as the sooner he was at the table, the sooner he could sneakily slide his tomatoes into Baby Ben's bowl without Mum noticing. Deco hated tomatoes as they made his lips feel all itchy and swollen. He remembered his teacher once telling him tomatoes were a type of fruit, which he thought was most peculiar, as they tasted much more like vegetables.

He leapt out of bed like a man on a mission and surprised himself at how familiar his new bedroom seemed already – all his belongings were in place, even the Barcelona scarf above his bed, and a football shirt and pair of shorts had already been laid out for him. He ditched his PJs in a crumpled pile next to his bed (knowing that Mum would have a good old moan later that he hadn't bothered to fold them), and faster than a snake striking its prey, he was sitting at the dining table, digging his fork into the world's most marvellous stack of sizzling sausages.

Considering that he had only just moved into the new house, he seemed to already have a thorough grasp of where everything was and felt quite proud of the confidence with which he had made his way downstairs straight to the kitchen. He had accidentally-on-purpose skipped past the obstacle of the bathroom. That was another thing Mum would probably have something to say about when she realised, but right now his sole purpose in the universe was to fill his empty stomach with the delights of the yummy breakfast.

The truth was, he couldn't bear the taste of minty toothpaste before tucking into a Full English anyway, and secretly thought his mum was a bit annoying when she harassed him about needing to brush his teeth *before* coming downstairs. Toothpaste ruined the taste of everything, especially apple juice (which he couldn't even bring himself to swallow when its taste was combined with peppermint). Yuk!

A few weeks ago, he had dared to argue with his mum, stating that it was pretty pointless to brush his teeth *before* breakfast. His dad had agreed, but Mum had gone on … and on … and on at them both about how it was crucial (whatever that meant) to look after 'those teggies'.

Deco hated it when she used baby talk to try and get him to do something he didn't want to do. He also hated it when Mum stood with a stopwatch, and insisted he spend a minute on his top 'teggies', and a minute on the bottom. Once she even bought a nasty pink sweet at the chemist and made him suck it until it left marks all over his teeth in the places he apparently wasn't brushing properly. Deco secretly thought that if he carried on brushing at this rate, he would have no gums left by the time he made his debut for Southford City!

Baby Ben was already sitting grinning in his high chair at the end of the table – he had an unfair advantage, as he was always carried to where he needed to be. Deco knew that when Baby Ben could finally walk, there would probably be an added element of competition to the Sunday morning dash to the breakfast table. He was already mentally planning out his route in the new house so that he could out-speed Baby Ben when the time came. He would need to experiment with different routes to find the quickest. Mind you, Baby Ben didn't seem bothered by the Full English yet – he was waving a plastic spoon in his right hand, gurgling to the sound of a nursery rhyme, and looking rather messy with the remnants of his cereal all over his face. Dad hadn't noticed, as he was sitting opposite the door scanning the back pages of the *Mail on Sunday*. He looked up and ruffled Deco's hair.

"Morning, son," he greeted.

Mum walked towards the table with a plate of fried eggs, and Deco waited gratefully as she served him one that was runny in the middle. She knew he liked to save the runny bit to dip his toast into.

"Why does Dad call this Full English, Mum?" Sarah looked at Deco, smiling proudly, as though his question was that of a genius child.

"I don't know really, but what a fantastic question! I suppose it's because, in the old days, working men used to start the day with a big meal like this, and it kept them going all day. It's full of nutrition, and the saturated fat it's cooked in is easily converted by the body into energy."

Deco smiled back at Mum, dribbling a little bit of tomato ketchup as he did so. He liked asking Mum questions as she always gave interesting answers, even if he didn't understand half of the big words she tended to use. It was times like this it was obvious that Mum was a doctor.

"It's very fashionable now for athletes to eat saturated fat instead of carbs for energy," Dad added helpfully, swallowing another mouthful. "I hear it's the best kept secret of cyclists and marathon runners."

"And footballers?" Deco questioned.

"Probably… Talking of football, you must come and see what I have done to *my* Wembley!" Dad exclaimed.

Deco tried to look interested, though thought Dad was sounding a little unrealistic. He didn't have the heart to tell Dad that the lawn would *never* look like Wembley though. So he nodded along, agreeing with the impossible possibility.

Deco quickly finished his breakfast (Mum told him to slow down and chew properly at least five times in the process), gulping his fruit juice before politely asking to be allowed to get down from the table. Mum loved it when he remembered his P's and Q's. At the old house, she kept a daily star chart to celebrate this. Deco hoped the removal men had forgotten to bring the boring old star chart.

He and Dad opened the glass door to the garden, and Deco gasped with amazement. The new football pitch-lawn was actually more like Wembley than Deco ever thought possible. Dad had cut it short, with beautiful, straight lines, starting at the edge of the slabbed patio in front of the house, and going all the way to the bottom of the garden. It was a masterpiece! Deco blinked to check he wasn't dreaming. When he opened his eyes again, he noticed that Dad hadn't just been content to cut the grass, but he had also painted a goal with white paint on the garage wall too. The goal was the same size as the goals at his old school.

To say this was incredible was no exaggeration. Deco now had his own football pitch-lawn and it didn't matter if there was no one else to play with – he could play against the wall without interference. He jumped into Dad's arms and hugged him as if Dad had just scored the winner in the Cup Final.

"I think I am going to love it here at your Wembley, Dad!"

5.

First Practice

Deco couldn't wait to get outside and play. The house at Southford was starting to become a distant memory now. He would happily move to a new house anywhere on the planet, even Outer Mongolia or the Antarctic, if it had a football pitch-lawn like this one!

He put his plimsolls on and found his futsal. Yes, futsal, *not* football. Deco had never really played with a proper football before, other than when his friend Bhavan had brought the special edition Champions League leather ball to school. Bhavan had ended up in tears as the leather was scratched on the concrete playground, so they had reverted to playing with a tennis ball instead.

Deco had been given a futsal as a present from Dad when he was small and had played with one ever since. He had actually played with the same kind of futsal at his after-school club in Southford, too. Dad and the coach agreed that it was the only real way to learn.

Deco hadn't been sure why it was *so* important to start with a futsal. He used to beg Dad for a real football instead, but Dad was absolutely convinced that all of the decent Brazilian footballers learned with this kind of ball, and that he would buy his son a full-size leather football when it was relevant to do so. Deco figured that if it was good enough for Dad's greatest hero, Deco, then it was good enough for him – the new Deco! According to Dad (and the coach back in Southford) the futsal was also much easier for kids because it was smaller and heavier than a normal football.

The coach thought the controversy over parents grumbling about his insistence on its use a real nuisance – a lot of the pushy dads wanted their sons to be playing with proper footballs, and Tarek's Dad (whose company did some work for Southford City) even sponsored the after-school club by donating a bag of Nike Ordem balls. Like all the other kids, Deco's jaw had almost hit the floor when he witnessed the arrival of the shiny new Nike balls. When he'd excitedly told his dad about what had happened, Joe had been really cross and insisted that they were a waste of time until he was much bigger and older. They had Googled the ball on the Internet that night and Deco had been staggered to discover that they cost £100 each. One hundred pounds! ... Deco secretly thought it must be an exceptional kind of football to cost £100.

After the incident with Tarek's Dad, the coach gave all the children a letter explaining the advantages of sticking with the system of using a futsal. Deco had learned the content of the letter off by heart, so he could tell his grandad all about it. The coach even collected signatures from all of the parents to confirm that they had read it and would therefore no longer continue to question his guidance.

There had been a couple of football terms in the letter that Deco had struggled with, but Grandad had taught him how to use a dictionary to find out their meaning. Now 'intercept' was one of Deco's favourite words. Once he fully understood the language of the letter, Deco realised Dad and his coach were right – if he wanted to play for Southford City one day, he would need to listen to their advice, and trust that all the best players started with a futsal. Probably even Neymar.

After the letter incident, Deco started asking Dad for advice on every detail of his football training. That's why he wore plimsoll trainers, unlike the other boys who always had the latest Adidas or Nikes. Joe had assured him that plimsolls were more lightweight than normal trainers, as they were made out of rubber with a canvas top. They weren't very good for wet grass but gave a solid grip on hard surfaces like AstroTurf. Deco had played with bare feet up until Dad enrolled him for the after-school club. Even then, sometimes they would play in the school gym with only gripper socks on. The coach said it helped with their touch and ball control, and Deco

49

knew he was talking sense, as gradually over time, he had started to develop skills that would put some of the Year 6s to shame.

It often felt like the ball was tied to him by a short piece of string, and that he could go right or left with his dribbling at any time. He was so comfortable with the ball at his feet, that he felt like he must have been born with it there. His mum regularly assured him that he wasn't, and that not everything in life had to involve a ball. Deco didn't agree. Nor did his dad … most of the time!

The futsal club only played five-a-side on very small pitches, so it meant that it was very important to keep running and losing your marker. It was also essential to make sure you were at an angle to the passer to be able to receive the ball.

"A bit like snooker," Dad told him. "It's all down to angles. The longer the distance you have to kick the ball, the more chance of something going wrong. Keep it short and simple…"

Practise, practise and more practise had been the story of Deco's short football life. He had been taught to practise something until he had mastered it, and to only move on when it became second nature to him. Sometimes it became a bit frustrating, and he'd moan to Dad about his longing to do a pretend penalty shoot-out, but Dad would shake his head and insist that being the best always required patience. Like most eight-year-olds, Deco found patience a bit of a chore, but tried to make a conscious effort not to whine and moan.

He had never really practised shooting at goal because in futsal, normally you would just pass the ball into the goal as the natural conclusion of passing with your teammates. Now, Deco had his own personal goal painted on the garage wall and could practise shooting all day long if he wanted to. He would need to be careful not to kick his ball over the garage, as it would probably fly over the fence and on into the sports field, and who knows where it would end up then…

Before starting to practise on his very own football pitch-lawn, Deco remembered watching a TV programme about David Beckham visiting some poorer communities where everyone loved football (and of course, supported Man United). Dad once told him that most disadvantaged children who lived in townships weren't very good at shooting, as they didn't dare practise the skill. If they missed the goal, and the ball went out of play, it would be the last they ever saw of it. Apparently, it was the norm for someone to steal the ball and run off with it for themselves! Deco had once had a nightmare about that and felt very sorry for the boys this had happened to. He couldn't risk losing his own beloved ball, so would have to be extra-specially careful!

Mum and Dad explained to him that they had a lot to do around the house that day, including unpacking the many boxes, so he could play in the garden until lunchtime. It was as if his birthday and Christmas had come at once! A Full English followed by a whole morning of uninterrupted football.

Deco practised and practised. He dribbled the ball with both feet, running and zig-zagging past imaginary opponents, before playing wall passes against the garage wall and receiving them back again. With one touch, he would turn and do the same again from another direction.

Never still for a moment, he was in another world – a make-believe world where it was his debut for Southford City against Man United in the Premier League. At the same time, he was running a full match commentary on everything that was happening. For two hours he ran and ran, never staying still for more than a few seconds, until finally, in his most grown-up commentator voice, he announced, "GOOOAAAAAAAAAAAL!" as he blasted the ball into the roof of the net. "Deco Cook scores the winner for Southford with the final kick of the game!" With that, he collapsed onto the lawn, absolutely exhausted, but fully satisfied. He wished he could do this *every* morning.

Throughout the morning Deco's skills had not gone unnoticed. Mum and Dad had been much too preoccupied to watch, but someone had observed *every* touch Deco made – *every* feint to one side or the other, *every* pass, shot, turn and step he made. Someone had even heard the running commentary, accompanied by infectious enthusiasm, and had witnessed the dedication and love Deco had for football.

Who was it? There wasn't anyone else in the garden. The gate was locked, and his parents and Baby Ben were nowhere to be seen.

Deco slowly rose from the ground, and as he looked up he thought he saw a movement through the window of the garden shed. He gingerly walked over and peered inside, but the small shed was empty aside from a few cobwebs and an old sweeping brush. He concluded that it must have been a trick played on his eyes by the reflection of the sun, and realised he needed some water as he was sweating buckets.

Just at that moment, he heard Mum call him.

"Daniel, lunch is ready." He turned towards the house. As Deco walked happily up the garden, he was once again taken up with thoughts of football super-stardom, and lost consciousness of the reflection behind him.

If he had turned around, he would have observed the existence of the crinkled face of a smiling old man in the window of the garden shed.

If he had turned around, he would have seen the man standing silently, his kindly, sincere eyes watching very carefully, until Deco disappeared out of sight...

6.

Sunday Promenade

Deco walked into the kitchen, went straight to the sink and ran the tap until the water was ice cold. He filled himself a large glass and guzzled it down without taking a breath.

"Be careful – you will drown at this rate!" Mum warned, chuckling to herself.

Deco wasn't concerned about drowning. He was more worried that he couldn't control the reaction of the water on his stomach. As the final drop entered his small body, he attempted to divert the inevitable problem by taking in a sharp breath of air. It unfortunately came out all wrong … as a loud BURP. Mum's chuckles quickly stopped and were replaced by a disapproving frown. He thought he could even see steam coming out of her ears, so with his conscience pricked he apologised.

"Pardon me for being so rude..." He didn't dare say the rest of the poem, as Sarah was glaring. "That was an accident, Mum. I didn't mean to do it. Pinky promise!" he pleaded cheekily.

Dad, never one to take offence to releasing trapped wind, couldn't contain his laughter, and sure enough, within a few seconds, they were all laughing – Mum, Dad, Deco and even Baby Ben.

Deco decided his mum was a lot less stressed at the new house, as when he had burped a few weeks ago at the old house, he had been sent to his bedroom to tidy it by way of an apology.

As they sat at the table for a sandwich lunch, they talked through their plans for the afternoon. Even though they had polished off a Full English only a few hours ago, Deco was as close to famished as he had ever been – he had used up so much energy on his football pitch-lawn. Deco concluded footballers must need to eat all the time.

Baby Ben woke up from a lengthy nap (Deco was sure he slept through most of life), and Sarah and Joe had unpacked their eighth box which was more than sufficient for one day, so Sarah suggested that they all go for a walk to explore the community. She called it 'A Sunday Promenade'. Deco hadn't a *clue* what she was talking about but noticed that she had used her posh voice to say 'promenade'. Both he and Dad knew that when the posh voice came out, it was Dr Cook speaking, and it would be unwise to protest.

"What a good idea, darling. I will go and shower and quickly clean up," Joe responded.

Before Deco could respond, Sarah continued in her posh voice. "And *you* can do the same, young man," she said, pointing to Deco's grass-stained knees. Joe and Deco trooped out of the kitchen towards the stairs.

"And Daniel, don't forget to tidy your room and put your PJs away … and by the way, clean your teggies!" Sarah exclaimed, replacing her posh tone with the dreaded baby voice. "Don't forget, one minute on the top, and one minute on the bottom. You can't come on our promenade unless your teeth are sparkling!"

Deco rolled his eyes and looked at Dad, who was rolling his eyes too. Neither could contain their laughter, and both took pride in the fact they were so alike.

"What does promenade mean, Dad?" Deco asked Joe when they reached the top of the stairs.

"I haven't got a clue, son, but we will do it, whatever it is. I don't think we have much of a choice anyway!" Dad replied. They both laughed again as they proceeded to their bedrooms.

Forty-five minutes later, the Cook family gathered in the hallway, having all scrubbed-up well and changed into smarter casual clothes. The way they stood around Sarah reminded Deco of school trips, where his teacher would call a register, peering over her clipboard suspiciously. He wondered if Sarah would do the same if she had a clipboard – she certainly liked organisation, and always thought he and Dad were up to no good.

Baby Ben was already strapped into his buggy and chattering happily away to himself. Joe locked the front door behind them, and pushed Baby Ben's buggy, with Sarah offering her hand to Deco. He felt himself go bright red – he was *far* too old to hold hands with his mum in public now. It would do nothing for his street cred with the other kids, if the first time they saw him he was being dragged along by Sarah. He pulled his hand away and Sarah got the message, so she held onto Joe's arm instead. The Cook family slowly walked up the driveway in the direction of the village green.

As they walked past the Medical Centre, Joe noticed the sign outside. "Look," he said, pointing to the sign in the car park, "Your mum's famous!"

They looked at the sign and saw the names of the doctors listed. "Dr Pridex..." Deco tried to read the names out.

"No!" Mum said, correcting his pronunciation: "Dr R Prideaux, Dr P Roach, Dr R Desai and Dr S Cook." Deco didn't like being wrong, but, nevertheless, was so proud of his mum that he almost wished he had held her hand after all.

"They didn't waste any time announcing me then?" Sarah blushed.

"I bet there's been a long waiting list for an appointment with a doctor, and they figured they'd keep the patients happy by telling them that you were on the way!" Joe jokingly replied.

Sarah had a sudden thought. "That's not so funny as it's probably true – you know what state the NHS is in at the moment." She had told Deco that this was the reason she was appointed to the job in the first place.

The new housing estate had brought hundreds of extra people to the village, and the Medical Centre couldn't cope with the numbers. Sarah suddenly felt quite nervous thinking about starting work the next day and imagined an endless queue of sickly patients waiting to see her. Joe squeezed her waist reassuringly.

As they continued walking towards the village green, they passed a similar house to their own, where an elderly man and woman were tending to their front garden. They both looked up and stopped what they were doing.

"You must be Dr Cook. Welcome to Glenrise!" the woman announced, smiling warmly. Sarah and Joe were a little taken aback that the woman seemed to know who Sarah was, and Deco watched their exchange with curiosity. The elderly man smilingly introduced them both.

"Tom and Ivy Bloor. Pleased to finally meet you!"

As the four adults shook hands, Sarah introduced the rest of the family.

"This is my husband, Joe, and this is Daniel and Baby Ben." Deco cringed to hear his mum introduce him as Daniel. He knew that if his dad had spoken first, he would have introduced him as Deco, but then he also knew that Sarah would have immediately corrected him with, "Daniel Edward Cook is his real name!" This would then be followed with Joe explaining that his initials were DEC, and the second letter of Cook was 'o', hence DECO was his nickname.

It was always the same pattern when they met anyone for the first time, and it never ceased to embarrass Deco, who hated it when his parents droned on. He was relieved that his dad kept quiet on this occasion.

Mrs Bloor was the next to speak.

"My Tom is *so* pleased to see you. Like everyone else in Glenrise, he's been waiting three weeks to see a doctor, and he still couldn't get an appointment with you until Thursday! He's had a terrible few months with his sinuses," she stated, looking very serious. Sarah inwardly shuddered. Her fears were justified. She could certainly expect to be very busy at her new job.

"See you on Thursday, Mr Bloor," she replied, as she forced a polite smile. The Cooks continued to walk along towards the village green, aware that the Bloors were watching them eagerly as they walked away.

They passed the streets of terraced properties on either side of the road, and saw that the last turning on the right, before the village green, had a number of small shops. They were about to cross the road and investigate when Joe noticed the ice cream van parked on the green. He suggested that they have an ice cream first and look at the shops on the way back – anything to avoid shopping! Deco immediately agreed with Dad, and surprisingly, even Baby Ben seemed to understand the proposition and started to laugh and jump up and down in his buggy.

"I see I am outvoted again by the three men in my life," Sarah responded good-naturedly. As they quickened their step towards the green, Deco ran ahead to secure a place in the queue for the ice cream van.

There were quite a few people on the green. The Cook family took their place near the back of the queue and waited patiently. The sun was still shining, and everyone seemed so friendly. People smiled at Sarah, greeting her as 'Doctor' as if they already knew her. She was quite self-conscious and felt anxious that so many people already knew who she was – she didn't like to disappoint anybody and found it quite overwhelming being presented with so many new names and faces.

The lady in the queue in front kindly explained that the Cook family photo had been in the Parish Community Magazine last week, together with an introduction to the family. The village knew all about them, even that Deco supported Southford City! Deco beamed with pride.

Another family joined the queue behind them – a man, his wife and their son. The boy was dressed in cricket whites and had obviously just finished a game. He was about ten years old, and Deco thought he looked a bit geeky with his ruffled curly hair, freckled face and glasses. No one played cricket in Southford – only the kids at the Grammar School. The boy's parents seemed very snooty to Deco, and he was amused as he listened to them introduce themselves as Mr and Mrs Opray and young Percy.

"I'm your Member of Parliament and represent your interests in Government," Mr Opray proudly announced. Deco wanted to laugh out loud when he heard the name, Percy, but bit his lip to stop himself. He stole a glance at his dad, who was also biting his lip and trying not to break into inappropriate laughter. Sarah ordered 99s all round.

"What's *your* name?" Percy turned to Deco and asked.

"This is Deco," Joe replied before Deco could answer.

Even though Sarah was paying for the ice creams, she heard and responded instinctively (in her posh voice, of course). "Actually, it's Daniel Edward Cook," and without blinking she carried on with her purchase of ice creams. True to habit, Joe responded with his explanation.

"His initials are DEC and the second letter of Cook is an 'o', hence DECO is his nickname." In this instance, Deco didn't mind that his dad had gone into so much detail.

Percy looked thoughtful for a moment. "How interesting," he observed, as Sarah passed 99s to Joe and Deco. "If I applied the same principle to my name, Percy Oliver Opray, that would make my nickname POOP…"

This time, neither Deco nor Joe could contain their laughter, and Deco nearly lost his flake from laughing so much. Sarah could not believe what she had just heard, and quickly took control of the buggy, ushering her boys away, and casting apologetic glances at the Opray family as she did so. The Oprays stood in silence, baffled by what had just happened.

When Joe and Deco were out of sight from the Oprays, they collapsed into uncontrollable hysterics. Sarah looked furious as she disliked teasing of this kind.

It took almost five minutes for Joe and Deco to stop laughing. Eventually composing themselves, they continued along the street, happily acknowledging the greetings of other people as they walked along at a leisurely pace. They looked a picture of ideal family happiness and contentment.

Deco had enjoyed the Sunday Promenade very much, even though he still had no idea what it meant.

7.

DR COG

Dr Sarah Cook: MB, DRCOG, DGM, DCH, MRCGP, or Dr Cog as Joe often teased, was a very talented young doctor. Deco had no idea why Mum had virtually the entire alphabet after her name, but he did know it meant she had passed lots of exams and had sat on many hospital committees in Southford. Sarah had studied and qualified at Newcastle University where she had met Joe, who was in the middle of a degree in Economics (which was something to do with the world – Deco wasn't sure what).

Sarah was a very bright and disciplined student, who learned quickly. She always did very well because she was determined and worked extremely hard. Joe liked to remind Deco that his mum's success was all down to her attitude. "She wasn't born with a silver spoon in her mouth," he used to say. Throughout her time at university, she had worked shifts as a waitress just to survive. Deco couldn't imagine his mum waitressing, but knew it was the truth, as Grandma had shown him a funny photo of a young Sarah wearing an apron and carrying a notepad, whilst sticking her tongue out at the camera. When she wasn't taking people's breakfast orders, she was sitting in the library, dedicating thousands of hours to studying.

"Deco, you have inherited the same hardworking qualities as your mum, but you have my eye for a ball," Joe often commented. Deco always felt good about that – he liked to have the best bits of both his parents.

Monday morning 7.45am arrived, and Sarah was dressed smartly in a blue business jacket and skirt. She kept flattening out invisible creases in her skirt, which struck Deco as quite odd, but Dad had already warned him she was nervous, and people do funny things when they're nervous. When she kissed the boys goodbye and left the house to walk to her new place of work, Deco ran to the window. He could watch her entire journey to work, as it was only next-door! He counted thirty-seven seconds exactly.

As Sarah entered the Medical Centre, the two ladies on reception made a high-pitched fuss over her, and practically carried her through to her room. Sarah wrinkled her nose as the smell of lavender was overpowering, and the women were a bit too touchy-feely for her liking. Sarah knew all of the procedures, and indeed the complete layout of the Medical Centre, having already visited on three separate occasions.

Sarah was always well prepared, and today was no exception, as she knew she was going to be extremely busy. She scanned her diary and saw that she had a full patient list through until 11am, and then a partners' meeting, followed by an induction programme with her secretary and the admin staff. Afternoon surgery was to start at 4pm through to 6pm.

After reading her diary, Sarah took a long swig of coffee from her thermal mug and smiled, feeling thankful that Joe had made it strong enough to see her through what was going to be a hectic day.

Sarah was restless as she tried to make herself at home in her new office. She really had no need to worry though. She was a super-qualified, young doctor with experience in pediatrics, geriatrics and child health, as well as her GP qualification. She already had a pile of correspondence sitting in her in-tray, and her computer screen was primed and ready to go as she looked through the notes on her first patient. After a brief scan, she pressed the button, and within a few seconds there was a quiet knock on the door as her first patient entered...

8.

Coach Cook

Meanwhile, next door at the Cook residence, Joe was busy loading Baby Ben into his buggy, together with all the things that were necessary to allow a baby to function comfortably whilst away from base (i.e. home). Deco was always amazed at the amount of planning that Mum and Dad would put into such excursions. It seemed that every possible eventuality was being accounted for, which was pointless in Deco's mind, as all Baby Ben seemed to do was sleep. This morning, the three boys were going out to explore the playing fields, and to visit the school to get a feel for their new area.

Joe was probably even more excited about his new job than Sarah was about hers. Although he qualified from university with a decent degree, his heart was always in football. He loved being out in the open air and hated being cooped up in an office all day long. As far as he was concerned, a new day was dawning for the Cooks, and this was the start of something very special. His work would soon feel like endless leisure...

Joe had continued to play semi-professional football all through his time at university and managed to get through the entire course without any student loans or other debts. He graduated at the age of twenty-one and went on to play professionally for Southford in the Football League, only ever suffering the odd knock or muscle strain, until that disastrous day when his whole life seemed to come crashing down. His knee was so badly damaged that it was obvious from the outset that he would never play professionally again.

He was heartbroken and didn't know what he was going to do without football. He and Sarah were recently engaged, and she had just gained her degree, so was about to take up her first placement at Southford General Hospital.

As a professional footballer, Joe was well insured against injury ending his career. He decided that if he couldn't play he wanted to become a coach, and so had set about a plan to make it happen. The plan resulted in him spending almost a year visiting and studying football academies worldwide, spending time at most of the top Premier League clubs, and the continental youth development specialists like Ajax of Amsterdam, Sporting Club De Portugal, Porto, Barcelona, Anderlecht and many more. He also spent time in the Brazilian favelas where he discovered 'futebol de salao' (futsal) which would prove to have a huge influence on his own football philosophy.

He was fascinated by how well young players in poor communities played football. He was already convinced on Anders Ericsson's 10,000-hour concept called 'The Role of Deliberate Practice in the Acquisition of Expert Performance', and now he was witnessing the results first-hand. These kids had nothing else to do but kick a ball … and they were *very* good at it. Joe followed up on the Brazilian trip by visiting the famous Right to Dream Academy in Ghana, and then a couple of the Jean Mark Guillou (JMG) academies in Africa and Europe. He really was a walking, talking encyclopedia of football knowledge!

By the end of Joe's travelling, he knew exactly what he wanted to do with the rest of his life. He had developed his own football philosophy based on his experiences and travels and was convinced it would result in the development of elite players. He needed the freedom and the platform to put his ideas into practice, and now he had found it – Glenrise!

9.

Stadium and Training Facility

Joe locked the door behind them, and he, Deco and Baby Ben set off to explore. Instead of turning left and past the Medical Centre, they turned right at the end of their driveway. The sky was a clear, pale blue, with just a few tiny puffs of white cloud in the distance. The sun was already shining brightly, and the high temperature justified the fact that all three were wearing shorts, tee-shirts and trainers. Not that it mattered to Baby Ben as he could barely crawl, let alone walk, but he still wore a small pair of trainers that he had inherited from Deco.

The entrance to the sports field was no more than a 100 metres from their house. A large white wooden sign next to the open gate announced in black capital letters 'GLENRISE RECREATION GROUND'. Just below, in smaller letters, it stipulated, 'No Dogs by order of The Parish Council'.

"What's a recreation ground, Dad?" Deco asked.

"It's an old-fashioned description for a sports field, but as far as we are concerned, this will be our very own stadium and training facility," Dad replied.

Deco had been excited seeing the fields and the AstroTurf court from his bedroom window but hadn't appreciated how big they were. As they entered the fields, he could see a full-size football pitch to his left, with full-size goals but no nets. The pitch was roped off from the rest of the field and looked as though it was very well cared for. It had two white-coloured dugouts on the halfway line for the coaches and substitutes. It was ultra-professional for an amateur village club.

Just a few metres away from the pitch, in the centre of the field, was another roped-off area with very short, almost invisible grass. The surface was extremely flat. This was obviously a cricket square. Deco smirked as he imagined that this was where Percy Poop and his friends spent their Saturday afternoons.

A few metres to the right of the square was another football pitch, running parallel to the other one, but far smaller. Deco instantly recognised it as the school football pitch. It had 213 cm x 488 cm goals – the same size as his old school, and indeed the painted goal on the side of the garage. According to Deco's dad, the pitch was 73 metres long, by 46 metres wide, the recommended dimensions of the football association for Under-12 9 v 9 games.

They turned right on the asphalt path and back towards their house. The path seemed to encircle the entire field. They followed the pathway along the side of their garden towards the fenced-off AstroTurf area at the top of the field, adjacent to the school. Deco was surprised as he reached the fence. It was as high as a tennis court, with floodlights on each corner. He was already familiar with the rubber crumb 3G surface from a birthday party that he had been invited to in Southford.

Wow! He couldn't wait to play on this.

Joe saw Deco's eyes sparkling as he stood and looked, first at the 'Astro', as Dad called it, and then, turning full circle, at the beautiful fields that they had just walked through.

"Not bad, eh?" Joe asked.

"Not bad!" Deco exclaimed. "This is fantastic … unbelievable. Why didn't we move here ages ago, Dad?"

Joe laughed and pointed to a picnic table under the shade of a nearby tree, which overlooked both the sports field and the school.

"Let's take a breather and chill a bit before we go and look at the school." They walked over to the table and sat in the cool of the shade. The sun was getting hotter and they were both glad they were in shorts. Baby Ben had fallen asleep again.

"How could he not stay awake for this?" Deco wondered.

"Dad," Deco said sheepishly, "You never explained to me about your new coaching business. Who will you be coaching?"

"Sorry, Deco," Dad smiled, "I thought you knew. I am going to run an after-school football club for children from your school and the nearby villages, just like your old one in Southford … only better!"

Deco beamed with excitement and wished he had asked the question weeks ago. He had been wondering what he would do to replace his old club where he had been so happy. He should have known his dad would never let him down. Dad knew how important football was to him and had always been there for him. After all, it was an interest that they both loved and shared.

Despite their love of the game, Dad never pushed him.

"Deco, it's your life. You should decide what you want to do with it. Parents should not try to relive their lives and dreams through their children," he always used to say.

He never really understood what Dad meant by this, although he had noted, on the very few occasions that he hadn't felt like training on a Saturday morning, neither Mum nor Dad had forced him to go.

"I wish I had the same choice about going to school," he often used to think. On those occasions he didn't train, he would still end up doing something fun, but given the choice, he would nearly always choose football.

"Dad, will I be able to train with you?" Deco asked excitedly.

"Of course – if that's what you want," Dad laughed.

"What I want?" Deco repeated in astonishment. "I want to be a footballer more than anything. How could you even think that I might not want to train with you?"

Joe found Deco's reaction amusing and predictable. He knew his son very well and continued the conversation in a slightly more serious tone.

"When I said that the after-school club would be better than your old one, what I meant was, it would enable boys like you to really follow your dreams if you want to be elite players. It will be called Glenrise Soccer Developments – GSD." Deco knew what elite meant and waited in anticipation as Dad continued. "For those with the self-motivation, who are prepared to invest the time in practice, I want to provide them with the tools and environment to fulfil their potential to become professional footballers. This can take thousands of hours of deep, repetitive practice, and I don't want that to be at the expense of their education ... or to be driven by pushy parents."

Deco was absolutely speechless for the first time in his life, and just gawped at his dad, hanging on his every word.

"We will train every day after school from 4 until 6, and Saturday mornings 9 until 1; a total of fourteen hours per week. In the school holidays, we will train Monday through until Saturday, from 9 until 1 daily, a total of twenty-four hours per week. Our target for each player is a minimum of 1,000 hours of deep practice per year. Trials start tomorrow, here on the AstroTurf, and I am expecting over 100 kids over the next three days for thirty places in GSD."

"Wow!" Deco exclaimed. He couldn't believe how much preparation Dad had put into it all. "Must I trial as well, Dad?" he asked.

"Of course," Dad replied with a smile. "Just because you are the Coach's son doesn't mean that you get special treatment." Deco jumped up laughing and gave his dad an enormous hug. He wanted to trial *so* badly and felt *so* excited he thought he would burst.

Joe had spent several weeks planning the trials by contacting all of the primary schools within a ten-mile radius of Glenrise. He had provided the schools with flyers for parents, promoting GSD, explaining the philosophy, times, costs and standards required, together with details of the three days of trialling. The response had been encouraging, and he was expecting at least thirty trialists per day.

Despite Joe telling Deco that he would not be getting special treatment Joe knew that his son had already received privileged treatment over the past four years. He was exceptional for his age and extremely self-motivated. He had already amassed over 4,000 hours of deep, meaningful practice and yet he had never ever played in an organised football game. In fact, he had never really tackled or been tackled before, as the philosophy he had been taught was to steal and intercept the ball. He had been schooled in exactly the same philosophy that Joe had developed in his quest to become a coach. It was through observing Deco's natural progress, without his dad's intervention that Joe became convinced of his own route forward, and Deco was the proof.

Deco had no idea just how good he was himself. Most of the boys at his after-school club had been older than he was. He had learned quickly and was very competitive.

Joe proceeded to instruct Deco on what he expected from him if he was to be successful at the trials. Firstly, Dad was to be addressed as Coach Cook by all players, including Deco. Secondly, his behaviour at all times should be respectful and above any criticism. Not that Joe had anything to worry about with Deco, because he had always had a great attitude, and neither Sarah nor he had ever had any reason to question it in public. The only concern for Joe was that, for the first time, outside of his old after-school club, others would see what an amazing talent his son was.

Deco had no problems with Dad's instructions and couldn't wait for the trials to begin the next day. As Joe finished talking, Baby Ben opened his eyes and started chattering to himself, breaking into a big, toothless grin as he recognised both Deco and Dad standing in front of his buggy. They set off through the gate that led from the sports field and into the school grounds. They passed the bicycle sheds and walked through the playground area and could see through the large windows into the classrooms. The school building was fairly new and very impressive. They came out onto the road and followed it until it joined the main road on the other side of the Medical Centre. The boys were hungry and ready for a mid-morning snack.

As usual, as soon as Deco had finished his snack and his drink, he was outside and kicking a ball about in his plimsolls. It was time for ball juggling. Every one of his after-school training sessions would start with ball juggling – a crucial part of the football philosophy he had been exposed to – and the *only* homework given after every session. Deco had been set a target of at least 2,000 ball touches a day since the age of five. Although it was always with a futsal, he could juggle a tennis ball almost as well.

He couldn't get the trials out of his mind and wanted to make sure he could execute all of the drills and skills he had acquired over the past four years. He spent the entire afternoon in deep, deep practice, before eventually finishing the session as he did the day before – making his debut for

Southford City against Man United in the Premier League, at the same time running the full match commentary.

"GOOOOAAAAAAAAAAAAL!" he finally announced in his most grown-up commentator voice, as he blasted the ball into the roof of the net. "Deco Cook scores the winner for Southford with the final kick of the game!" With that, he collapsed onto the lawn, absolutely exhausted.

Once again, Deco had been observed throughout the afternoon.

If he had turned around, he would have observed the existence of the crinkled face of a smiling old man in the window of the garden shed.

If he had turned around, he would have seen the man standing silently, his kindly, sincere eyes watching very carefully, until Deco disappeared out of sight…

10.

The Trials – Day One

Deco was beginning to find getting up in the morning a problem – sometimes a BIG problem, especially to Mum who would often (half-playfully, half-seriously) try to drag him out from under his covers. The truth was, he loved to lie there in his bed for as long as possible – it was so cosy and warm. Today, however, was completely different to any other ordinary day…

It was the first day of trials.

Deco was up at 6am sharp, showered, dressed and looking like he meant business in his football kit. He was sitting eagerly at the breakfast table by 6.20am, and was proud that, as he suspected, he hadn't even needed his alarm clock to wake him. The adrenalin from the excitement about the trials had turned him into a machine!

When Mum and Dad came downstairs at 6.30am, sleepy and in need of coffee, they weren't at all surprised to see Deco sitting there impatiently. After all, he would *always* be up at the crack of dawn on Saturday mornings before training (but they both secretly thought that 6.30am was probably an all-time record). Mum kissed him on the forehead as she went to switch the kettle on.

"Hi Danny, up early to help your mum with the chores before she goes to work, or have you got other plans?" she teased him. Dad laughed.

"Mum, this is the most important day of my *entire* life. I can't do chores. I am going to be a professional footballer," Deco blurted out.

"Yesterday was the most important day of *my* life, but I still had to feed Baby Ben, dress him, make breakfast and get myself ready for work. Life goes on regardless, and there are responsibilities. Maybe you would be kind enough to share the load with me today and empty the dishwasher?" Sarah responded mischievously.

With a long, frustrated face, Deco got up from the table and reluctantly opened the dishwasher, only to find it empty. He turned to face Mum and Dad, and realised immediately that he was being teased.

"Relax Deco!" Dad said, laughing again, "or 'chill out' as you youngsters say. Today is important, but it isn't a matter of life and death. It will be okay."

Deco looked at Dad closely and was instantly relieved to see his face was filled with sincerity. If Dad said everything would be okay, it definitely would. Deco cheerfully turned his attention to his breakfast.

Sarah left at 7.30am with Baby Ben, who was about to start his own three-day trial at nearby Glenrise Nursery. Sarah was also due to start morning surgery at 8am. She kissed Joe and Deco goodbye.

"You'll have a fantastic day, I'm sure," she reassured them. "Enjoy it, and make sure you tell me all about it later."

Joe and Deco loaded the car with some of the equipment that was needed for the trials, and left the house soon after, driving the short distance around to the school. Deco helped Dad unload the boot. He carried two large bags of futsals around to the gate of the Astro, where he saw a table and two chairs positioned outside, and a sign pinned to the table saying 'Registration'. There were also lots of chairs in a single line about five metres away from the fence, running parallel to it.

The gate was unlocked and slightly ajar as they walked in and deposited the balls and other items against the wire fence. Deco knew the Astro surface was big but hadn't appreciated quite how big. It was nearly as big as the school football pitch. It had markings for four futsal pitches, and was set up ready for play, with the goals in position and each pitch numbered on the fences to the side of the pitch – 1 through to 4.

Joe told Deco he could warm up for twenty minutes, whilst he set up everything ready to receive the trialists. Deco leapt into action starting with six circuits of the astro, and a few stretching exercises, before taking out one of the balls and doing some juggling. Although the trials were due to start at 9am, the first boys started to arrive about 8.30am. Joe suggested at that point that Deco should sit outside of the Astro and wait with the others. Dad gave him a red bib with the number 16 on it.

Deco watched as the first boy registered. It was the boy's mother who spoke first. "Alex Adams from Glenrise," she stated.

"Good morning both. Please take this blue bib," greeted Joe. "As you are the first to arrive, Alex, you can be number 1. Please take a seat over there until the others have arrived." At the same time Joe applied a tick to his list of names. There was now a steady stream of boys arriving, mostly with either their mums or dads, and some who had clearly car-pooled and travelled together with one adult. Joe repeated the same greeting and instruction to them all, alternating between allocating numbered red and blue bibs.

Deco was very impressed with Dad's organisation of it all. He put everyone at ease and seemed completely in control of what was going on. Deco secretly thought his dad could be the next Pep Guardiola.

The boys were a complete mixture of height and size, even though the oldest of them was still only ten years old, just about to go into Year 6.

"Some look like giants!" Deco mused aloud. One boy in particular looked as if he was at least thirteen. He had heard him give his name as Peter Black, from Kirby. He was also clearly popular with some of the other boys, as Deco observed him with a group of about six or seven trialists, who all greeted each other and did a handshake they had clearly copied off the TV. Most of them were bigger boys as well. Deco was beginning to get a little nervous now, and 9am was fast approaching, but he knew that it was healthy to experience nerves before a game.

"It makes you more alert, and gets the adrenalin pumping," his old coach used to say. Deco didn't have a clue what adrenalin was, but he knew it was obviously something important for footballers.

Coach Cook raised his voice above the chatter and asked for attention. There must have been about fifty people, including adults, although there were still two or three boys who hadn't arrived. He started by repeating his earlier welcome to everyone, and then explained how the morning was going to work.

"All boys have a numbered bib. Listen carefully," he instructed. "If you have a number 1 through to 4 bib, you will be playing on pitch number 1," he said, as he pointed to the pitch. "If you have a number 5 through to 8, you are on pitch 2," again pointing to it.

"I think you guys are all smart enough to have got the gist by now," he added. "So, it follows that 9, 10, 11 and 12 are on pitch 3, and anyone with a bib from 13 onwards is on pitch 4."

Deco could see that everyone seemed to understand, as they were already looking at each other's numbers. Deco noted that Peter Black was a blue 13, and some of his friends were also high numbers. Deco's stomach lurched as he realised he was going to be on the same pitch as them.

Coach Cook paused for a few seconds, looking around to confirm everyone knew what they were doing and seemed satisfied.

"All of you guys need to know exactly what I am looking for today, and that is a set of characteristics, competences and abilities, which we can develop." He continued, "You may ask – 'what do you mean?' My answer would be – quickness of feet, touch, speed over the first few metres, vision, awareness, intelligence and, most importantly, your character and willingness to learn."

There was silence as all the boys looked at one another nervously, but also great excitement at the opportunity.

"At the end of the session, I will be inviting the successful boys to come back on Friday morning at the same time," Coach Cook added. "So … let's get started."

11.

The Drills Begin

Coach Cook gestured for them to follow him through the gate to the pitches, and Deco started psyching himself up for the challenge ahead. He wasn't going to let the bigger boys make him feel any less of a player!

As they entered the Astro, Deco noticed that they had all obeyed the Coach's instructions (not like at school!) and were wearing futsal trainers, Astro shoes or conventional trainers. Deco and one other boy, with ginger hair, were the only ones wearing canvas plimsolls. By coincidence, the ginger boy was wearing red bib 13 so would be in the same group as Deco.

All of the boys walked briskly to their designated pitches and waited for the Coach's guidance and further instructions. When they were all clearly in position Coach Cook explained that for the first part of the morning they would be practising drills and set routines. Later, they would move on to 4 v 4 games before Coach Cook announced the callbacks for Friday. Deco could almost smell the anticipation in the air.

Coach Cook suggested that they should all introduce themselves to the players on their pitch, as good communication was essential if they were to work as a team. Deco was always fascinated when Premier League players shook hands before a game. They never seemed overly friendly, yet after a game, opposition players would often hug. Dad told him that it wasn't unusual for players to be a bit stand-offish before a game, as footballers tended to be 'in the zone' until the final whistle, and sometimes even longer if it had been a really tough game.

Deco was on pitch 4 and the big boy, Peter Black, was the first to speak to the others.

"As you all probably know, I'm Peter Black, the captain of Kirby boys Under-11's," he smugly announced. "We are the best Under-11 team in the county." Deco was taken aback by his cockiness and had to be very careful not to screw up his nose in disgust. Peter continued oblivious to his lack of audience, "This is John Smith and Harry Hurst – they also play for Kirby." They all had that same sickly, smug smile. Deco took an instant dislike to them. All three were in the blue team and all three had turned up in shin guards. Coach Cook had a quiet word with them to take off their shin guards, as they wouldn't need them.

The fourth boy was a much younger, smaller, ginger-haired boy. Deco had noticed him waiting patiently next to an almost identical twin who also had ginger hair. He was the boy in the plimsolls. Deco immediately felt a sense of identity with him and liked the fact he wasn't trying to show off like the Kirby crew. The ginger boy and girl both had short ponytails, so it was difficult to tell them apart. The ginger boy nervously introduced himself.

"I am Gheorghe Mutu. I am eight years old and live in Glenrise," he said in a heavily accented voice. Peter and the other two Kirby boys burst out laughing and Deco noticed Peter trying to make a mockery of him by putting on a silly foreign accent. All of the other boys joined in the laughter, except Deco. If anything, he was seriously impressed that English obviously wasn't Gheorghe's first language, yet he could communicate far better than the stupid Kirby crew.

What none of the boys knew was that Gheorghe, his twin sister and their parents had only moved to England from Romania a year ago. In Romania they had been very poor and came from a tiny community in the far north west of the country: a small town called Bicaz. There was no work for Gheorghe's mother or father despite their willingness to do any job they could in order to feed their family. They lived in an area called Dodeni, which was nothing more than a run-down ghetto with no electricity and extremely cold winters. Gheorghe's dad had a friend who had found work in a distribution centre in Glenrise and had been promoted to Supervisor. He sponsored the family to come and join him there, and even found Gheorghe's mother a job, too. Now the Mutu family lived in a council-owned property in the village. It was like paradise compared to the harsh conditions in Dodeni.

Both Gheorghe and his sister had embraced life to the full since moving, and they loved Glenrise. Gheorghe was particularly good at maths and was already working in the gifted group at school. His sister was a brilliant artist, and her drawing of Big Ben was on display in the school reception area. The teachers had a soft spot for the Mutu kids, and they were both very happy, almost always wearing a broad smile on their faces ... even when being poked fun at.

The three boys in red bibs, the same as Deco, introduced themselves one by one. The first was a tall boy of dual heritage from Glenrise called Matt Dalglish. Then there was a Chinese boy, Li Chun Wan. All of the other boys seemed to know Li, and Deco thought it was perhaps the coolest name he had ever heard. His parents ran the Oriental Star

Chinese Takeaway in the village. The third boy was a black Afro-Caribbean boy called Kipp Bell from the village of Houghton. He was also quite tall for a nine-year-old, a fact that Deco was to find out later. Last but not least, it was Deco's turn and he decided to be brief and to the point:

"Hi, my name is Daniel, but my friends call me Deco. We've just moved to Glenrise from Southford." None of the other boys realised that Deco was the Coach's son.

At that point, Coach Cook gave the boys their first one-touch passing drill of the day in their teams of four. 'Short, short, long' was the sequence as he walked from pitch to pitch correcting technique and watching carefully. They continued until he was satisfied that they had perfected the exercise as best they could, and then went on to another passing drill of 'short, short, short'. Again, he walked from pitch to pitch correcting and advising. It was now forty minutes since the session had started and many of the boys were showing signs of fatigue and lack of concentration.

Deco heard Peter Black moan: "This is boring – kids' stuff. We did this at Kirby when we were seven years old. When are we going to play a game and show what we can do?"

Deco also heard other boys moaning, and even picked up on the occasional mutter of words that would have definitely earned him a mouthful of soap if he had used them. Coach Cook was also fully aware of the disquiet.

"Okay, that wasn't bad. Let's see what you can do with an increase in tempo. Same drill but hit the pass harder," he instructed, smiling to himself. It was carnage! There were balls all over the Astro and boys colliding with other boys trying to retrieve them. After about five minutes of utter chaos Coach Cook shouted, "Stop! Get some water and have a breather." He sat them all down on the Astro, and as they gulped their water and wiped their sweaty brows, he said very calmly, "You boys want to become professional footballers, don't you?"

"Yes, Coach," they all responded in unison.

"Well," he replied, taking a deep breath, "You won't get there unless you push yourselves. Do you know that the English Premier League, along with the Spanish La Liga, are the fastest leagues in the world? Players get an average of 1.1 seconds on the ball. If a player can't receive the ball at pace, control and pass on within that timescale, they are dead!" He paused, and all of the boys seemed really surprised.

Coach Cook went on: "So, if you want to go all the way to the highest level, you have to start now, get the foundations right and build on them through increasing the tempo. It can't be done overnight. It takes hours and hours of deliberate practice and repetition to get there. If you are selected for this project you will have a target of 1,100 hours per year of deliberate practice on top of your school commitments. So, my advice would be, if you are not up to the sacrifices you will have to make in order to fulfil your dreams, you should get yourself new dreams!" The boys gasped in shock. Most of them weren't used to being spoken to so bluntly.

"Okay, on your feet, lads! Let's go again with the same drill," Coach Cook shouted. So, they all raced back to their pitches to carry on. By now many had already subconsciously made their minds up that they didn't want the discipline in their lives that Coach Cook was talking about. They simply couldn't be bothered.

They carried on with drill after drill with Coach Cook observing and advising throughout the morning. It was already obvious to him which boys had potential. He had planned to finish the session with twenty minutes of 4 v 4 games with no goalkeepers.

"Okay guys, stop what you are doing and go and get some water!" Coach Cook instructed. As the boys helped themselves to water many just collapsed onto the Astro with exhaustion. He continued, "This is the part you have all been waiting for – the opportunity to play a game and show what you can do. Let me make it easy for you and tell you now that I want to see you put what you've learned today into practice within a game scenario. I want to see quick passing, good movement and intelligence. We have just one rule – NO TACKLING!"

There was another familiar gasp of surprise from most of the boys, then Peter Black put his hand up to attract the attention of Coach Cook.

"How can we defend our goal if we aren't allowed to tackle?" he asked. His tone was really rude, and it made Deco quite angry. He wondered how his dad would handle it. He need not have worried.

"A good question, young man," Coach Cook responded with ease. "I want to see you use your intelligence with good positional play when you haven't got the ball and look for the opportunity to steal the ball and quickly turn defence into attack."

This concept was completely new to the majority of the boys and in particular, to the boys who played organised football for the Kirby team. Their coach had been a fearless central defender as a player and was an advocate of tough tackling. As a result, Kirby defenders probably spent more time on their backsides than on their feet. However, it had proved to be a successful strategy because they were undefeated in the past two seasons and had gained quite a reputation for themselves.

"The boys who have been on pitches 3 and 4 can sit it out and watch the boys on pitches 1 and 2 to begin with," Coach Cook continued. "Then after ten minutes they can play and the boys from 1 and 2 can watch them. We'll repeat the process with all teams playing for twenty minutes in total. Let's go – blues against reds on both pitches." As they started, the other boys watched with keen interest to see what the competition for places was like.

The competition would be tough!

12.

Game On

The two games started tentatively, with all the players trying to impress with their ability, and with what they had learned during the morning. Coach Cook was pleased with what he saw, as most boys showed that they had absorbed his coaching to varying degrees – some very well, and others not quite so well, but it was easy for him to spot the four players who were standout performers across the two pitches. The boys who were watching also found it easy to spot the better players, although they were surprised at some of the Kirby players who, despite their reputations, were not very good at completing their passes on these small pitches.

After ten minutes, the two games stopped for their half-time break, and the boys took to pitches 3 and 4 to start their games. The players had already decided amongst themselves which positions they would play. Deco and Li were to play just in front of Matt and Kipp.

The blues lined up, with Peter Black in the middle of a line of three, and his Kirby teammates either side of him, to the right and left, with Gheorghe playing in front of them. The blues started with possession; the three Kirby boys looked quite composed, passing the ball backwards and forwards between themselves, and little Gheorghe made run after run, trying to lose his marker without receiving a pass from the Kirby boys. They were clearly inviting the reds to come and try to get the ball away from them.

Li was the first to put pressure on by positioning himself in front of John Smith, preventing him from moving forward with the ball. Unfortunately Li was unable to deal with the feint to the right, and John's sudden movement to the left, as he danced past a hapless Li. Deco went to cover Li to block his run. As he slipped the ball inside, Peter Black thumped it into the net. 1–0 to the blues!

On the restart, Deco passed the ball to Li, who immediately came under pressure from Harry Hurst on the right. He panicked, and tried to pass to Matt, but didn't hit it hard enough. Gheorghe pounced on it, taking the ball past Matt and placing it wide of a lunging Kipp, into the back of the net. 2–0 to the blues!

"Well done, Mutu!" shouted Peter Black, with a vague trace of respect in his voice. The reds were clearly up against a good team.

"Mutu, Mutu, MUTU!" chanted the watching boys enthusiastically. His sister was grinning and clapping her brother.

"Is that your twin brother?" one of the adults asked, "He's soooooo good!"

"Yes, he is, but not as good as me," she replied and laughed, without taking her eyes off the game.

The game got under way again, and the ball was once again intercepted by the live-wire Mutu, who passed it back to John Smith. Deco was on to him like a flash and stole the ball from under his nose. Peter Black moved quickly to block Deco, who left him for dead, sitting on his backside – a familiar position for the Kirby boys. Deco neatly slotted the ball home to the applause of those watching, many of them very happy to see the cocky Peter Black brought down to earth. Peter, on the other hand, wasn't so happy:

"Try that again, kid, and you will end up over the fence," he threatened Deco out of earshot of anyone else. Deco did not respond. 2–1 to the blues.

Straight from kick-off, Peter received the ball and went strongly forward in a determined manner, moving like he would crush anyone in his way. He was bearing down on Deco, as Deco slipped out of the way, stealing the ball at the same time. With one touch and a tap forward, he found the feet of Li, totally unmarked in the space vacated by the over-extended Peter, who couldn't miss. 2–2!

This was a game changer. The Kirby boys were angry and embarrassed by Deco and became uptight. Mutu continued to be a handful, snapping at the feet of the reds at every available opportunity. He was like a pesky little wasp! Fortunately for Deco's team, the other Kirby boys were guaranteed to flap under the same pressure. Deco was able to steal the ball twice more, setting up goals for Kipp and Matt, who were both settling into the rhythm now with some very good passing and support techniques, creating angles for Deco to find them, almost by instinct. As Coach Cook signalled half-time, the score was 4–2 to the reds. Despite being amongst the youngest, both Deco and Mutu had impressed *everyone* watching.

13.

Decision Time

The second half got underway on pitches 1 and 2, and the four boys who impressed during the first half continued to impress and cement their places in Coach Cook's mind. He noticed that they were all Year 5 boys, a year older than Deco and Mutu, who would both be in Year 4 on their return to school in September.

The boys from pitches 3 and 4 watched with fascination, although some were still quite moody at being made to look ordinary by Deco's team. Peter Black was moaning at Mutu.

"If you did more running, Mutu, we would be winning easily!" Peter said accusingly. The other two Kirby boys seemed to agree with their captain. Mutu was puzzled by the accusation because he knew the truth. The Kirby boys were not as good as they thought they were.

As soon as the games finished on pitches 1 and 2, the games restarted on 3 and 4. Coach Cook hadn't been very impressed with the standard of football on pitch 3, and no one had really caught his eye. He concluded that most of these boys had made up their minds that they didn't want to be part of the project after all.

However, pitch 4 was a different story. All of the boys could play. Deco and Mutu were outstanding, and Kipp, Matt and Li all showed potential. Peter Black and the Kirby boys were also quite accomplished, but they would be Year 6 next term. They were older than the others, more experienced by playing regularly for Kirby, though their attitudes were proving to be a real hindrance. Joe thought that they might be disruptive and would probably want to continue playing for Kirby anyway. That wouldn't work.

The football being played on pitch 4 continued to impress both the boys and adults watching alike. The red team ran out winners by nine goals to five. Deco was the stand-out player. Everyone was talking about the new boy. It was one of the parents who eventually worked out his identity, recollecting the article on the Cook family in the Parish Magazine. The news quickly spread amongst those who were watching.

Deco had scored a further three goals in the second half, and Li and Matt one each. Mutu scored all three of his side's goals, capping a very good performance. The Kirby boys, with their chins hanging, were visibly very disappointed as the game ended.

All of the boys gathered with their parents and other spectators outside the fenced Astro.

Coach Cook warmly thanked the boys for coming, then went on to announce the successful trialists...

"The boys I would like to come back on Friday morning are ... from Pitch 1, Alex Adams and Sanjay Singh, Pitch 2, Kevin Shearer and John Bremner and from Pitch 4, Gheorghe Mutu, Matt Dalglish, Kipp Bell, Li Chun Wan and Daniel

Cook. Once again, I would like to thank you all for coming."

The crowd clapped spontaneously and gradually dispersed, leaving behind a few of the successful boys who were smiling and excitedly chattering amongst themselves. Peter Black's ego was bruised, and the other Kirby boys were embarrassed and disappointed, but tried to give the impression to those around that they didn't care, and, in any event, would rather stay training and playing for Kirby!

Coach Cook and Deco set about clearing up all the equipment and were the last to leave. Neither spoke a word on the short journey back. As they pulled up onto the drive they saw Sarah pushing Baby Ben in his buggy towards the side entrance of the house. Sarah stopped and waited for Joe and Deco, who both looked tired but had big smiles on their faces.

"I take it this morning went very well for you both by the look of those grins?" Sarah asked knowingly.

Deco could not contain himself any longer. "I made it, I made it, Mum! I am going to be a professional footballer!" he blurted, as he ran into his mum's outstretched arms. At the same time Joe gave them both a quick hug and turned his attention to Baby Ben, as he pushed the buggy through the door.

"Come on, little fella, your big brother will be hungry after all the excitement," he said. Deco couldn't stop talking throughout their late lunch.

He was reliving every moment of the morning, fuelled with elation and enthusiasm. His mum was left in no doubt that Daniel was now totally committed to their move to Glenrise. The Cook household would sleep well tonight!

14.

Trials – Day Two

Wednesday – Day Two of Trials – started in almost identical fashion to Day One in the Cook household. Deco slept a little longer but was still downstairs for breakfast, just behind Mum and Dad. He had gone to bed the night before just as excited as he was on Monday night. He slept surprisingly well and was itching to get back on to the Astro.

"Dad, will I be allowed to trial again today?"

Dad smiled at Deco. "Why would you want to son?" he asked. "You have already been selected as one of nine successful trialists. You can watch carefully and check that I don't miss the next Ronaldo."

"But Dad, I want to train and play just like yesterday," Deco responded disappointedly.

Deco's mum joined in. "Your Dad is in a very difficult situation, as everyone knows that you are his son, and he doesn't want to compromise himself by giving you preferential treatment." Two strange words there for Deco – 'compromise' and 'preferential'. He had heard them before but didn't really understand their meaning.

"But Dad, I *am* your son and you *are* my Dad," he replied, with a puzzled look on his face.

"The only way this can work is if I show no nepotism and treat you like I treat all the other kids. Likewise, you need to address me as Coach because that's who I am on the football field," Coach Cook, not Dad, replied.

"Nepotism?" Now Deco's mind was completely blown! He looked at his mum and dad with an even more exasperated, puzzled stare.

Mum and Dad both burst out laughing, realising that he hadn't really grasped the situation properly, and hadn't a clue what this new word meant.

"Nepotism is a word which means 'showing favour to a close relative when that person doesn't deserve it over others'." Mum continued her explanation with a question to Deco. "You don't want the other boys to think that you are there just because you are the Coach's son, do you?"

Now that he understood, Deco felt mortified at the mere suggestion and quickly agreed with Mum. "Of course not! It would be so embarrassing if anyone thought that." Dad laughed before making his response.

"Thankfully everyone can see what an excellent player you are, Deco, but you and I still need to demonstrate a professional relationship on the football field, the same as I have with the other boys. I' ll be Dad again, as soon as we step off the field." With that, Joe gave Deco a reassuring hug. Deco clearly understood the message and would surely always remember the word 'nepotism'!

"We need thirty-two boys when it comes to the final session when we play 4-on-4," Dad added. "If we are short of players, perhaps you can make up the numbers?"

Deco thought about this for a moment…

"Dad, maybe you should ask one of the other boys watching before you ask me – then I won't be embarrassed," Deco said cautiously. Sarah and Joe burst out laughing again, as Sarah hugged her son proudly. Deco eventually joined in the laughter, too.

Sarah and Baby Ben left the house as they did the day before, making their way to the Nursery. Sarah then continued on to the Medical Centre. Joe and Deco had left the equipment in the car overnight, saving the effort of having to reload it. They made the short journey around the block and repeated the unloading process of the day before, with Deco carrying the two large bags of futsals around to the Astro. Everything appeared to be the same as the day before. The registration table was in the same position as were all the chairs. The gate was, again, slightly ajar as Deco entered carrying the bags, followed closely by his dad carrying a stack of cones. Deco placed the bags on the surface.

"Coach, is it okay if I get warmed up while there isn't anyone else here?" he enquired politely. Joe laughed again. His son had certainly got the message – that is, if he wasn't just trying to be clever and sarcastic!

"Of course you can, Daniel," he replied, in his Coach voice.

"Coach Cook, I am not Daniel on the football field. I am Deco!" he grinned cheekily as his dad playfully chased after him.

As on the previous day, the boys started arriving promptly at 8.30am; each boy registering individually; each receiving a coloured bib, red or blue alternately; then taking their seats and waiting enthusiastically. Deco was the first to be seated, followed by a familiar face from the day before, who sat down beside him without registering at the table. In fact, there were two of him ... or so it seemed. Deco blinked. They were almost completely identical, apart from their clothes. It was difficult to recognise any difference, even up close, as they were the same size, had the same ginger hair with a short ponytail and the same smiling faces.

Deco greeted the twin who sat down beside him. "Hi Mutu, is this your sister?"

The twin gave him a mischievous smile, feigning insult. "Are you stupid, English boy? Do you not know a girl when you see one? I am Nadia and he is Gheorghe!" she replied. After a brief silence and embarrassment at Deco's expense, the twins burst out laughing as Deco's face turned crimson.

"I am sorry, my friend," chuckled Mutu, "she always jokes this way." Deco's embarrassment was immediately put at ease as he joined in the laughter. However, in reality, Deco could have been forgiven for his mistake because it was only with very close scrutiny that you could spot any difference at all. They both wore football kit – Mutu all white, and Nadia a white top with black shorts. They both wore black plimsolls. The most visible, obvious difference was the pair of white pearl studs in Nadia's ears.

Nadia remained silent whilst the two boys talked about the previous day's trials. At the same time, they were excitedly watching today's hopefuls arrive and register. Nadia interrupted:

"I know him, and him," she whispered loudly, as she pointed to two boys about to sit down. "I run rings around them in the playground at school. I steal their ball with my feet and they chase after me. They always think it is Mutu but it is me … his sister," she emphasised more loudly. The two boys obviously heard her jibe – as did at least twenty other people – and they scowled out of embarrassment.

Although Deco didn't realise it at the time, Nadia had a chip on her shoulder as a result of being a girl in a predominantly boy's football world. She often faced prejudice, and yet she was almost as good as Mutu, having kicked a ball about together since the age of three. They had nothing else they could do in the slums back home in Dodeni. They lived in a one-room flat on the fourth floor, with no heat, light or water. They slept in the same room as their parents and could only survive the winter nights by huddling closely together. There was no nursery or school for them, so they provided their own amusement and played football, every hour of every day. In winter, it was the only way they could stay warm. The only thing they had to amuse them was each other, and the small abandoned warehouse they played in. That is until they met Ilie!

Ilie was a man in his forties who claimed to be an ex-professional footballer. He, too, lived in a flat near them. He had no work and always seemed very unhappy. During the day he would go to the warehouse, along with a few other kids, and would show them the things to practise. He used to tell them that the only way to get out of their poverty was football and they should dream big and aim to play in the English Premier League one day. They should practise, practise and practise even more if they wanted a great future. None of the other kids took much notice, except for the twins, who listened to his every word and followed his drills and special advice. Football became their motivation for survival. Ilie disappeared after a couple of years and was never heard of again. People said that he was a fraud and a drunk and had nothing to offer. The twins knew otherwise! They continued practising as if he was at every session watching them, as he always had been.

Coach Cook called everyone to order, and repeated the same instructions as the day before, almost verbatim. All the boys marched eagerly to their allocated pitches and awaited instructions from the Coach. He started them off with the same drill sequence as on Tuesday – short, short, long, followed by short, short, short.

After forty minutes or so, he witnessed the same whispers of discontent and stopped the drill. Again, as he did the day before, he instructed the boys to put more pace on the ball and then resumed the drill. Once again, utter chaos and carnage prevailed: balls and boys everywhere. Coach Cook smiled knowingly. It was all part of his coaching plan. They stopped for a breather and he delivered the same impassioned lecture as the day before, and received the same shocked response from the boys as on Day One.

"Okay, on your feet lads! Let's go again with the same drill," Coach Cook shouted and they all sprang to their feet.

Deco had counted that there were only twenty-nine boys trialling. That meant his dad would be three short when it came to the last session of 4 v 4 games. Maybe, just maybe, both he and Mutu would get a chance to play.

He just wanted his dad to ask Mutu first...

15.

Decision Time – Day Two

"Okay guys, stop what you are doing and go and get some water!" Coach Cook instructed just as it approached midday, almost to the exact time as Day One. As the boys helped themselves to water, many just collapsed onto the Astro with exhaustion, as they had the day before. It was time for the trialists to play a game. Coach Cook gave the same instructions as the day before, and there was a murmur of surprise when he said "NO TACKLING!" There was no Peter Black-type character there on Day Two, although there were two or three boys from Kirby. Coach Cook had already noticed one of them on Pitch 1 who looked quite promising. He was a Year 5 boy by the name of Mo Khan.

Coach Cook explained, once again, the procedure of 4 v 4 and the schedule. All of the boys seemed to understand exactly what to do and Pitch 1 and 2 players demonstrated their eagerness by leaping to their feet and quickly moving to their pitches. Coach was correct when he said it was exactly what they had been waiting for!

The boys from Pitch 4 looked at one another knowingly. They were three players short. There were only two players in red bibs and three in blue. The two boys in the red team were the boys that Nadia had embarrassed at the start of the session. Coach Cook had already noticed he was three players short on Pitch 4 earlier and had looked towards the spectators to see if there were any familiar faces from the day before. He spotted the Mutu twins, sitting with Deco, and made a mental note that he would ask them to make up the numbers on Pitch 4. It was time to communicate that to them. Coach Cook turned to face the spectators, who were sitting about five metres away from the Astro fence.

"I wonder if you, Mutu, and your twin brother might join the red team on Pitch 4 … and Daniel, perhaps you would play in the blue team?" he enquired.

This was exactly as Deco had wanted. His dad had not embarrassed him, but he was to get the opportunity of another game. All three smiled and nodded as Coach Cook thanked them, turning around to get the two games underway. Nadia could not stop smiling while Deco and Mutu both looked at each other wondering if they should have told Coach Cook that Nadia was a girl. Nadia had made sure they remained silent, by giving them both a sharp elbow in their ribs, as the Coach asked them to play. Neither Mutu nor Deco was brave enough to prevent Nadia from having this opportunity, nor were the two boys in the red team on Pitch 4. They all kept quiet, knowing that the Mutu twins would torment the opposition with their skills and that would be good for them, too.

Deco and the Mutu twins stretched and started a short warm-up before joining their teammates. Without bringing any attention to herself, Nadia slipped her two pearl stud earrings into the small kit bag she shared with her brother.

As the first two games commenced, everyone was concentrating on what was going on in the games. Coach Cook had already concluded that most of today's successful players would come from these two pitches and he wasn't at all disappointed with the standard of play. He blew his whistle for half-time and the four teams left the pitches to seek water and rest. The players on Pitches 3 and 4 took up position and waited for the whistle to start play. None of the blue team knew that Nadia was a girl as they had never seen the twins before. All three boys were from the neighbouring village of Houghton.

The whistle signalled the start of the two games on Pitches 3 and 4. Deco received the ball straight from kick-off and delivered a defence-splitting pass to one of his teammates who had an open goal. As he pulled back his right foot to strike the ball, it was gone. Nadia had stolen the ball, and with another touch, had already slipped it to her brother. As Deco closed him down, Nadia moved to his left and took the return pass. She skipped cleverly around the last defender and calmly placed the ball in the net. 1–0 to the reds!

"Wow!" thought Deco, "She can play!" He had never seen a girl play football like this before.

The twins ran riot.

Deco didn't see much of the ball in the first half and it was the same story in the second half. His teammates were quite slow and couldn't react quickly enough to combat the Mutu twins. Even the other two boys in red looked promising with the live-wire Mutus buzzing around. The game eventually finished with the reds scoring ten goals but the blues only four in reply. The Mutus scored all of their side's goals between them, with the twin in the black shorts finishing top scorer with six goals.

Coach Cook was very impressed with the games on pitches 1 and 2, though a little disappointed with the boys on 3 and 4; that is except for the two Mutu kids, and Deco and an

Indian boy on Pitch 3. He couldn't really tell the difference between the twins but that wasn't an issue as they both showed enough promise for the project. He did wonder why he only had one application for Gheorghe and not for his twin brother. "Perhaps it's an issue of cost and the parents can't afford to send both," he mused.

All of the boys gathered with their parents and other spectators outside the fenced Astro, as the Coach repeated the procedure from Day One.

"I would like to thank you all for coming today. The standard was, again, very high. I appreciate that those boys who are not invited back to Friday's session will be disappointed, but they should not be deterred. It doesn't mean that you don't have the potential to be good footballers; it's just that you didn't make it today because of the high standards displayed by others. We will be trialling again during October half-term, so who knows? Use this extra period of time to develop your skills by constant repetition and practice, and it might be your chance to impress next time."

There were echoes of agreement and encouragement from the other adults as Coach Cook announced: "The boys I would like to come back on Friday morning are … from Pitch 1 – David Todd, Mo Khan and Chelsea Moore. Pitch 2 – Peter Greaves, Andy Speed and Jimmy Lampard. Pitch 3 – Ravi Seth, and finally from Pitch 4 – Gheorghe Mutu's twin brother." He finished with, "Once again, I would like to thank everyone for coming today."

The crowd clapped and drifted away slowly. The successful trialists were overjoyed and chattered with excitement. Deco watched the Mutu twins as they spoke to one another in what he assumed was Romanian. They hugged each other, with their customary big smiles filling their faces, until Deco brought them down to earth.

"Coach doesn't know that you are a girl. What are you going to say?" he asked. The twins quickly sobered up and their smiles disappeared. Both looked uncertain as Coach Cook appeared and approached them. "Well done, you two. Which one is Gheorghe?" he asked.

Gheorghe hesitated…

"It's me, Coach Cook," he responded timidly.

"So, what's the name of your twin brother?" Coach asked, looking at Nadia and offering his hand to shake hers. She shook hands firmly, looking him in the eye with that cheeky, mischievous expression that she had shown to the woman the day before.

"Nadia, Coach," she replied as she waited for his reaction…

Coach Cook continued to smile until the penny dropped.

Nadia was a girl!

16.

Trials – Day Three

What an eventful day Wednesday had been – the boys-only football project had already unearthed a talented pair of twins. But there was a problem. One was a girl! Or was that even an issue? Joe had never experienced this situation before.

Throughout his short coaching career Joe had never been exposed to women playing football. He knew how popular the game was for girls in America, making it the biggest participation sport in the USA, despite the dominant NBA, Baseball and American Football leagues. He had been faced with a dilemma the previous afternoon and was now pondering over what he should do. The decision to select Nadia was as easy a decision as it was to select Gheorghe, as he told them both as soon as he realised she was a girl.

"Why should it make any difference? She was there on merit," he stated. Their faces lit up with joy, as did Deco's, when Coach confirmed that Nadia was *in the pick.*

Thursday, Day Three, proceeded as smoothly as the previous two days of trials had. It took on exactly the same format with thirty-three boys starting. One of the boys had to leave early so there were only thirty-two boys to play in the 4 v 4 games. The only change in Coach Cook's repertoire was at the end when he talked about more trials in October.

"The half-term trials in October will be open to both girls and boys. Each trialist will be given the opportunity to be selected for a place in the project on merit alone," he added.

Deco sat and watched with his two new friends, as he had the day before. There were another seven or eight boys who had been successfully selected on Days One and Two and they sat close by, watching optimistically, as their friends also trialled. The standard was as high as it had been over the past couple of days but there wasn't anyone who stood out quite as much as Deco had on Day One. They all assumed Deco's special skills were because his dad must be a brilliant coach. Surely, *they* would be as good as him if he were to be their coach, too…

Coach Cook chose another eight boys from the Day Three trials, increasing the number to twenty-five in total, to return on Friday for a morning of induction before the project commenced on Monday. Twenty-four boys and one girl! He announced the names as before: "Pitch 1 – Gino Banks and William Dean. Pitch 2 – Robbie Charlton and John Haynes. Pitch 3 – Charlie Barnes and Murdock McCoist, and from Pitch 4 – Dickie Best and Will McNeill.

Of the additional boys, three in particular caught Deco's eye. Gino Banks, who despite only being nine years old was a big boy with strength; Dickie Best who looked as if he would be a tricky winger; and Charlie Barnes, an Afro-Caribbean boy who was tall, leggy and like lightning.

Nadia was delighted with the way the three days had turned out. She never dreamed on Day One that she would be sitting there, alongside her brother, as a successful trialist. She thought back to the days that Ilie would encourage them both to practise, practise, practise. He had been proved right all along. He may have had his problems with drink but, as far as she and Gheorghe were concerned, was a brilliant coach who definitely knew what he was talking about. She wondered where he was and what he would say if he could see them now. In the excitement of the last twenty-four hours, she had temporarily overlooked that she was a girl. So, she reached into her kit bag, found her pearl stud earrings and wore them again with pride.

Deco discovered that the twins lived just around the corner from his new house, so he asked his dad if they could come and play after lunch. Dad agreed, and Deco invited them both, explaining that he lived next to the Medical Centre. The Mutu twins helped Coach Cook and Deco carry the equipment back to the car and hitched a lift down to the main road, where they jumped out and politely thanked Coach Cook for the ride in his vehicle.

"Nice kids," Joe mused to Deco, as the twins walked in the direction of the village green. "They've had some good coaching somewhere in the past," he added.

After lunch there was a knock on the kitchen side-door and Deco opened it to see the two cheeky, smiling Mutu twins.

"Dad, they are here! We are going to play football on the football pitch-lawn," Deco shouted.

"Okay, I have some work to do here but I will be watching you to make sure you don't fall into any bad habits!" his dad joked.

The three kids smiled excitedly and went through to the back garden. The twins gasped when they saw the size of the 'football pitch-lawn' and the goal painted on the wall.

"Wow!" they both squealed in unison, as they thought back to the warehouse in Dodeni.

They played all afternoon, breaking only occasionally for water. Deco showed them some of the drills he had learned from his previous coach that he had practised, practised and practised over and over. Coach Cook watched the three of them play. He was delighted that Deco had found a couple of kids of the same age, who shared the same passion for football. The Mutu twins were certainly very highly motivated and talented little footballers with good attitudes. He smiled when he thought back to the previous day when he mistook Nadia's gender, but watching them now, he was glad he had made the error. She was impressive, with well above average ability, as was her brother. Deco was further advanced than they were, but Joe was well aware that Deco was extraordinarily talented for his age.

Joe wasn't the only one looking on that afternoon. *Every* touch, *every* feint, *every* pass and *every* shot that the energetic trio made was being silently witnessed and warmly appreciated...

Exhausted after almost three hours of play, the children collapsed onto the lawn almost breathless. The church bells were ringing in the distance and, slowly getting to their feet, each one turned, looked at the shed and was somehow drawn to it. Peering inside, nothing could be seen other than cobwebs and an old sweeping brush. They looked at one another in puzzlement, but at that moment Coach Cook was calling them from the kitchen. They wandered back towards the house as if nothing out of the ordinary had happened, and none of them mentioned the strange experience again.

If they had turned around, they would have observed the existence of the crinkled face of a smiling old man in the window of the garden shed.

If they had turned around, they would have seen the man standing silently, his kindly, sincere eyes watching very carefully, until they disappeared out of sight…